RED PETTICOATS

and
OLD GLORY

A Parable of Freedom

by **DEAN BLACK**

Springville, Utah

ISBN 0-929283-06-6

Manufactured in the United States of America

Cover art by Rick Sutter.

Contents

To my wife and children, who inspire me
to honor the principles of freedom.

Foreword

"Ideas are often poor ghosts; but sometimes they are made flesh: they breathe upon us with warm breath, they touch us with soft responsive hands, they look at us with sad sincere eyes, and speak to us in appealing tones; then their presence is a power, then they shake us like a passion, and we are drawn after them with gentle compulsion, as flame is drawn to flame."

With these words Silas Marner, many years ago, described Dean Black's book, *Red Petticoats and Old Glory*.

You are the same today as you'll be in five years except for two things: the people you meet and the books you read. When you finish Part One of this beautiful story of God, country, and family, you will be different. You will be more thankful for your family, country, and troubles than ever before. When you finish Part Two you will want to start over again to see if you can experience the same beautiful pictures and emotions this story inspires. I promise the second, third, and fourth readings will be even more Tremendous. You'll discover with a sixth grader a new dimension of freedom. You'll appreciate the influence of a teacher as never before. You'll get a wonderful history lesson that will be more exciting than any television special. You'll visit with Ben Franklin, Viktor Frankl, Helen Keller, and Isaac Newton. They will give many old truths a bright new look that will bring smiles to your face, warmth to your heart, and tears of joy to your eyes. Being a grandfather, I could not help but think of my grandchildren. They will identify with Robby, the sixth grader, as I do. They too will be different as they see our history unfold, discovering the wonder of our heritage and a new meaning of freedom they might never have known had it not been for this book.

Charlie "Tremendous" Jones

Here is my creed. I believe in one God, the Creator of the Universe. That he governs it by his Providence. That he ought to be worshipped. That the most acceptable service we render to him is in doing good to his other children. That the soul of man is immortal, and will be treated with justice in another life respecting its conduct in this.

— *Benjamin Franklin*

Prologue

Benjamin Franklin smiled, and with good reason. The Council had approved his plan. They'd called it "highly unusual" (which it was), but they'd also seen its merits. They were as enthusiastic as he was!

The plan *was* good. It met basic Council requirements, and all the pieces fit. Implementation would begin on April 17, 1990—exactly two hundred earth years from the day Ben died. Choosing the bicentennial of his own graduation was a small detail, and meaningless, really. But it was a typical Franklin touch, and it gave a certain tidiness to the plan.

The boy he'd chosen was ideal. Robby Barton was twelve years old—old enough to understand, yet young enough to believe, both of which were critical. Understanding was the very point of the plan, after all, and Robby would have to *believe* just to get it started.

Even the emotional context was exceptional. Robby's father was out of work, which was by itself a major assignment. But the bank was also foreclosing on the family's home, which raised the potential value of the assignment considerably. Coping with such a complex assignment would be difficult, truly it would, but such was the nature of mortal life. The difficulty of an assignment *always* matched the magnitude of the treasure available within it, and to get the treasure, people had to accept the assignment it was based on. That was fundamental.

But Mr. and Mrs. Barton weren't accepting the assignment! They were *resenting* it, as if it were tragic instead of divine. They were obviously fuzzy-headed when it came to understanding the purpose of mortal life. But they would learn.

In the meantime, the Barton children, Robby in particular, had adopted their parents' misinformed point of view. This wasn't a problem, however, because they all had strong fundamental desires, even if their sense of purpose was temporarily off course. As long as their desires were sound, such a difficult assignment could serve in the long run only to focus their courage. Even now, it had opened Robby's mind to serious reflecting, and it would incline him to accept the invitation that would launch his part of the plan. The *drive to understand* was there, and that would prove to be the key.

Of course, the Council had imposed the usual condition—that the past not be changed in any meaningful way. The plan would bring peace to Ben's dear friend Nicholas Herkimer, and it would inspire character in the boy and wisdom in his teacher. But those changes met Council requirements, for they would foster love and joy in the people involved, and they would be achieved without the tiniest hint of compulsion or deceit.

As a bonus, the plan would set in motion a wonderful adventure! The mortals involved were great and noble beings, though they hadn't quite grasped that yet, and they had some growing yet to do. Ben proposed nothing more than to place them in a circumstance where the cost of *not* growing would be too great to accept. And then, Ben knew, they would grow into heroes, because they would refuse to be anything less.

PART 1

Robby

April 17, 1990

10:30 a.m. Mrs. Elliott held aloft a ragged-edged chunk of gray concrete that was roughly the size of a book. All but one of her sixth graders angled their heads to see it.

"This is a piece of history," she said. "A piece of the Berlin Wall. I want you all to experience it, so gather around me in a group."

The students stood and began moving forward. She held the chunk toward them, revealing bright streaks of paint.

"As you can see, people wrote on the wall what they felt about it. Who were those people? Can you imagine what they felt—what the wall meant to them?"

Mrs. Elliott gave the chunk to Lacy Gordon, a wide-eyed girl with braces, who accepted it with an expression of awe. Robby Barton, a small, blond boy who was usually eager to learn, hung back, other things on his mind.

"I want each of you to experience this piece of history," Mrs. Elliott continued, "so please pass it around. Look at it closely. Feel its texture. Draw it into your senses. Make it come *alive*. Open your hearts and minds to it. See if you can capture what it really represents."

One by one, the students examined the chunk. They *experienced* it (Robby excepted), just as Mrs. Elliott had requested. They rotated it here and there, exposing every surface. They angled it *just so* to catch the light. They poked their fingers into its chinks and crannies and cracks. Ricky Simmons even *smelled* the chunk, and Emma Scovill clasped it to her bosom and closed her eyes as if receiving some heartfelt message from another time and place. Meanwhile, the room buzzed with excitement.

The excitement didn't touch Robby Barton, however. His brain couldn't keep up with it. Thoughts entered and left before he could grasp them. Heaviness squashed him, pushing everything out of him, leaving him blank and empty and distressed. So when Eric Seymour gave him the chunk, he just passed it to Amanda Wilson and sat back down at his desk.

What's happening to my family? he thought. *Where are we going to live? And what . . . what will happen to my dad?*

The room settled again into silence. Mrs. Elliott placed the chunk on her desk and turned to face the class. "Tell me your experiences," she said. "What did that chunk of concrete mean to you?"

"Freedom," said Devin Engle. "The people broke down the Berlin Wall because they wanted freedom."

"All right," Mrs. Elliott said. "It represents freedom. But what does freedom *mean?* Be more specific. What exactly were those people looking for?"

"To be able to live wherever they choose," said Jeannie Mollner.

"To be able to *say* whatever they choose," said Kenneth Watkins.

"And to vote for their own leaders," said Cindy Nash.

"Yes," Mrs. Elliott said, "they wanted all of those things."

It was at this point that Ben Franklin's plan began to take effect. The Council had given him permission to inspire within Mrs. Elliott's mind a certain thought, which he now did. As a consequence—and much to her own surprise—Mrs. Elliott continued by saying, "And they wanted freedom to lose their jobs, *or even to lose their homes!*"

Robby's head popped up. *Freedom to lose their homes?* The heaviness fled from his mind; intense curiosity took its place. *Freedom to lose their homes?*

Mrs. Elliott turned toward her desk and picked up the concrete chunk. She looked at it inquisitively, her mind groping for new thoughts. After a moment she replaced the chunk, then turned again to her students and began walking between two rows of desks.

"Did you know that communist governments *give* people their homes and their jobs? They *give* them medical care and everything else they need. The people own nothing, but they lack nothing, or so the theory goes. When those people tore down the Berlin Wall, they fled from *guaranteed security* to a life where they can fail, and where every day they risk losing everything they have. How can such a risk make them free?"

She paused, but no one answered. When she reached the end of the aisle, she crossed behind the last desk and began walking up the next aisle toward the front of the room.

"Even today many of the people who first fled to the West still don't have jobs or homes. Some of them don't want to cope with the responsibility, but many of them, even without a job or a home, *still* count themselves free, and joyfully so. How can that be?"

Mrs. Elliott stopped and scanned the rows of

desks. Finally a timid hand arose.

"They can *look* for a job," Julie Ralston said. "For whatever job they want."

"All right. They're free to look for a job. But if they can't find one, are they still free?"

No one raised a hand.

Mrs. Elliott proceeded to the end of the aisle, turned to face the class, and found herself instantly drawn to the third desk in the second row. Robby Barton sat staring at her with an intense look in his eyes. She'd noticed sadness earlier, but it was gone, replaced by . . .

Ben now implemented step two by inspiring within Mrs. Elliott what she took to be a mere hunch.

"Robby," she said, "has your father . . . lost his job?"

Robby's intense look vanished. His shoulders slumped, and his eyes dropped to his desk.

"Forgive me, Robby," Mrs. Elliott said, walking toward him, "but I feel that I must know."

Robby said nothing.

"Your father *has* lost his job, hasn't he?"

"Y . . . Yes."

"And are you about to lose your home?"

"Yes."

"Is that why you've been so sad this morning."

Robby choked back a sob. "Yes."

Mrs. Elliott crouched beside him, her eyes level with his.

"You don't feel very free, do you."

For a moment, Robby said nothing. Then, in a whispery voice, he said, "I feel terrible."

The room was still. Mrs. Elliott stood, returned to

her desk, and leaned back against it, her mind still groping for bearings. "This isn't the lesson I'd expected to teach," she finally said. "But it's a good one."

She walked again to Robby's desk and touched his shoulder. "Robby, may I ask you a favor?"

Robby nodded without looking up.

"I want all of us to think about this lesson tonight. And when we come back to school in the morning, I'd like to use your situation as an example. I mean, you could tell us what you're experiencing, and we could talk about it and try to understand how freedom really works. It's important, Robby, and you could help us a great deal, because any one of us could be facing tomorrow what you're facing today. What do you think? Could we do that?"

Robby looked up, uncertainty clouding his eyes.

"It would help you understand, Robby. You *would* like to understand, wouldn't you?"

Robby stared at her for a moment, and then, almost imperceptibly, his bearing lifted, the uncertainty began to fade, and the intense look grew again in his eyes. "Yes," he said. "I'd like that. I'd like that very much."

10:30 p.m. Robby sat in his bedroom at the desk his father had built. Gentle light bathed him from the lamp on the wall. On the desk lay a writing pad; his right hand held a pencil that doodled occasionally and tapped now and then, but mostly remained still.

He heard a gentle knock. "Come in," he said.

His father entered. "I was just heading to bed when I saw the light under your door. I thought I'd see if you needed anything. You okay?"

"Yeah. I'm just trying to figure something out."

"Can I help?"

How can he help when he's so unhappy? "No thanks, Dad. I'll be fine."

"Okay. Well, get to bed soon. I'll see you in the morning."

"Dad?"

"Yes?"

"Don't go."

Robby's father closed the bedroom door and sat down on the bed. Robby turned his chair to face him.

"We talked about freedom in school today because Mrs. Elliott had a piece of the Berlin Wall. We said people broke down the wall because they wanted to be free, and she asked us what freedom means. Well, I thought I knew, but then she said freedom means being free to lose a job, or to lose a home, and that doesn't make sense to me. You lost your job, and now we're just unhappy. Tomorrow we're going to talk about it, and I've got to figure it all out. I've got to figure out what freedom means."

"I see," his father said.

They sat in silence.

"Robby?"

"Yeah."

"I think I've let you down."

"Hmm." Robby stared at the floor.

"I haven't handled things very well."

Robby twisted the shirttail of his pajamas.

"Look, Robby. I know what Mrs. Elliott means. But it's hard to put into words. And it's hard to remember . . . especially when you're going through something as scary as what we're going through. But Robby, I promise you. I'll help you understand. We won't let this situation get out of hand. We may lose our home, but we won't let it get us down. Okay?"

Robby looked up and tried to smile. "Okay, Dad."

"Now, why don't you go to sleep and let this sit awhile in your mind."

"Okay. Thanks, Dad. I . . . love you."

"I love you too, Robby." He stood, kissed Robby on the forehead, and quietly went out the door.

Robby turned out the light and knelt beside his bed. "Dear God," he said. "You know what's happening. My dad's out of work . . . and we might lose our home. . . . I don't understand it, and I'm scared. . . . So's my dad, I think, even though he tried to make me feel better tonight. I want to understand what's happening to us, so please help me. Thanks."

11:45 p.m. The prayer was Ben's cue, but he let Robby sleep for an hour before he approached Robby's bedside and gently shook him. Robby sat straight up.

"What?! Who are you? What do you want?"

Ben turned on the lights and smiled.

Robby smiled back. "I know you! You're Benjamin Franklin. I've seen you on TV commercials."

Ben laughed. "You're a child of your times, Robby. May I sit down?"

Robby scooted over to give him room, and Ben sat beside him on the bed. Ben, more serious now, said, "I'm sorry to awaken you, Robby, but I want to ask you a favor."

"What do you mean?"

"You've got a problem, and I do too. I think we

can help each other."

Robby hesitated. "H . . . How?"

"You want to understand what freedom is, right? I've got a friend who knows more about freedom than just about anybody. We used to sit and talk about freedom, and he even taught *me* a thing or two. Now, my problem is that I've got to send my friend a very important message. If you became my messenger, you could deliver my message and ask him your question all at the same time. What do you think?"

Robby thought about it. "Well, I suppose I could do that. Who's this friend of yours?"

"His name is Nicholas Herkimer."

"Nicholas Herkimer? Does he live around here?"

Ben laughed. "No. He fought in the Revolutionary War—at the Battle of Oriskany."

Robby's mouth dropped. "The Revolutionary War?! How can I talk to somebody who fought in the Revolutionary War?"

"You just go back and talk to him."

"But how?"

"All you have to do, Robby, is *believe*."

"But I don't understand."

"You don't have to understand, Robby." Ben thought a moment, then said, "Look, I'm here, aren't I?"

Robby stared at him. "It looks like it."

"Well, if I can come here, you can go there. Same principle."

"I . . . uh . . . I still don't understand."

Ben became very thoughtful. "Have you ever been trying to figure something out and just felt *stuck*—like right now? So you go to bed, and when you wake up, you know the answer? Has that ever happened to you?"

"Yes."

"So where did you get the answer? I mean, did it come to you, or did you go somewhere for it?"

"I don't know."

"You see, you don't know how it happens, but it happens anyway. That's the way this is. You just have to believe in it. Do you know any reason *not* to believe?"

Robby thought about that and couldn't think of a reason, so he shook his head.

"Well, there you are. You've got a question, and if you just fall asleep, you'll have your answer when you wake up, just the way it's happened before. So when you're off getting your answer, I'd like you to give Nicholas Herkimer my message."

Robby scrunched his nose and cocked his head. "That's all there is to it?"

"Yes. That's all there is to it. Now, go back to sleep." Ben stood. "Oh, I almost forgot. Here's the message."

He took an envelope from beneath his shirt and gave it to Robby, who tucked it into the waistband of his pajamas. "Now, Robby, what I'm about to say is extremely important. As soon as you give Nicholas Herkimer the message, you must return immediately."

"But how will I find him?"

"When you wake up, you'll be at Fort Stanwix in New York State. They know him there. Just ask around."

"Why can't you come?"

"I'll be in Paris trying to rally French support for our cause. I can't be two places at once, can I?"

Robby giggled. "I suppose not."

Ben hugged him. "So go to sleep. I'll see you when you get back."

August 5, 1777

8:30 p.m. A British army surrounded Fort Stan-wix,[1] artillery in place. General Barry St. Leger, leader of the British force, planned to launch his attack the following day. Within the fort's headquarters, around a crude table strewn with maps and lit by candlelight, three patriot leaders were discussing their strategy.

Fort Stanwix stood in east central New York State between the Mohawk River and Wood Creek, guarding the entrance to the Mohawk Valley. General St. Leger wished to pass through the Mohawk Valley on his way to Albany, where he would join his colleagues, General John Burgoyne and General William Howe, in a large pincer movement designed to trap the bulk of the American forces against the eastern seaboard. Only the patriots of Fort Stanwix stood in his way.

The commander of the patriot forces was Colonel Peter Gansevoort.[2] His second-in-command was Lieutenant Colonel Marinus Willett.[3] They were aided by Lieutenant Colonel Mellon of the recently arrived Massachusetts regiment.[4] As the three officers planned their defense, a knock interrupted them.

"Come in," said Gansevoort.

A soldier with a frustrated look on his face entered the room dragging a young boy.

"Oh, Manning. Come in," Gansevoort said.

Gansevoort turned to the leader of the Massachusetts regiment. "Colonel Mellon, this is Corporal Manning, my best scout. I sent him to find out what the British are up to."

He picked up a candle and walked around the table for a better look at Robby, who held a broad-brimmed felt hat across his chest and shifted uncomfortably in flax-colored knee britches and a sun-bleached linen shirt. Gansevoort held the candle close and looped his finger through Robby's single suspender. "And who is this?" he said.

"I don't know, sir," Manning said with an aggravated tone. "I found him wandering just outside the fort. I asked him where he came from, but he won't answer."

Willett smiled. "British spies are young these days."

Gansevoort stooped to meet Robby at his level. "Who are you boy? And what are you doing here?"

"C . . . C . . . Can you tell me where I can find Nicholas Herkimer . . . sir?"

Manning gave an exasperated snort. "You see, sir! That's all he says."

Gansevoort held up his hand to calm Manning down. Turning to Robby, he said, "What do you want with Herkimer, boy?"

"I've got a message for him . . . and I want to ask him a question."

"Who's the message from?"

"B . . . Benjamin Franklin."

The patriots laughed, and Gansevoort raised a calming hand again.

"Tell me, boy. Why would Benjamin Franklin want to send a message to Nicholas Herkimer?"

"They're friends."

This time even Gansevoort laughed.

"Nicholas Herkimer's just a local farmer, boy. And Benjamin Franklin's never been in these parts."

"But . . . can you tell me where I can find him, sir?

Please?"

"He's coming this way now, about ten miles away, I suspect, heading up the south side of the Mohawk River. If he makes it, you can see him. If he doesn't make it . . . well, perhaps none of us will see him again."

"But I've got to see him, *now!* Please tell me how to get there?"

Gansevoort stood. "I haven't got time for it, boy. You'll just have to wait. We've got work to do." He gestured to an empty corner. "Sit over there. We'll deal with you later. Anyhow, you won't meet Herkimer unless you wait for him here."

Robby went to the corner and sat down while Gansevoort turned his attention to the business at hand.

"Manning. Let's hear what you have to say. What sort of trouble do we find ourselves in?"

The men gathered around the table again, and Manning began to explain. "As far as I can tell, sir, the enemy army consists of about 1,500 men. Most of them are Indians fighting under Joseph Brant."

"Brant!" Willett snapped. "That renegade? I suppose John Johnson's probably there as well."

"Yes, sir," Manning said. "Johnson's commanding about 350 Royal Yorkers. But I believe his main goal is to mobilize the Tories in the valley and get his property back."

Mellon interrupted. "Who are these two . . . this Brant and Johnson?"

Gansevoort answered. "Brant's the most powerful Indian in this territory."

"Indian?" Mellon said, surprised.

"That's not his real name, obviously. He's full Indian, but he was raised by Sir William Johnson. He took on the name Joseph Brant and went to white schools in Connecticut. Now he's organized several Indian nations to fight against us. Only the Oneida and the Tuscarora remain on our side."

"Who's this Johnson fellow?"

"John Johnson is Sir William Johnson's son, so he and Brant are practically brothers. Sir William used to own the second largest estate on the continent. Only William Penn's was larger. John Johnson inherited it, but his views weren't very popular here, so he left it all to go to Montreal to join the British. He wants to help the British beat us so he can get his land back. The British probably brought him along because he knows the valley, and he knows all of the loyalists who stayed behind. If he can get them together, he could double the size of the enemy force."

Manning spoke up. "There's Hessians, too, sir. Probably eighty of them. And about two hundred regular redcoats. As I said, that's about 1,500 men altogether, and they've pretty well got us surrounded."

"Who's in command?" Mellon asked.

"The redcoat commander is General Barry St. Leger," Gansevoort answered. "They've been here three days now, laying in supplies and artillery. My guess is that they're going to come against us tomorrow."

Gansevoort left the table and began to pace in the shadows, pensive, his hands behind his back. The other men watched him almost stumble over Robby's heavy, square-tongued brogans; heard him pause and kick absentmindedly against the leg of a bench; then saw him walk to the window facing the parade ground and stare through it into the night. Finally, he returned to the table and put the palms of both hands flat against it as he leaned over the maps.

"As I see it, gentlemen, here's our situation. Burgoyne's right here." His right index finger thumped the map. "His redcoat army is coming south from Montreal." His finger traced the line. "At the same time, General Howe's coming north from Philadelphia, and they plan to meet here"—the finger thumped again—"at Albany. That's where our forces are quartered under General Schuyler. If they take Albany, they'll have cut New England from the rest of the colonies and trapped a third of our population and most of our strength against the sea. Now, this force that we face here under General St. Leger is probably a diversion—a flanking operation."

Willett said, "Quite so, sir. Burgoyne just took Ticonderoga. Saratoga's next. If St. Leger gets past us here at Stanwix, he'll head straight for Saratoga and flank our army from this side. That will split our forces, and Saratoga will probably fall. Then it's just a short step from there to Albany. And if Burgoyne and Howe rendezvous at Albany, the Revolution may be over."

Gansevoort thumped the table solidly with his palm. "Gentlemen, we alone stand in their way. To get to Saratoga, St. Leger has to pass through our Mohawk Valley. Fort Stanwix must stand. St. Leger must not be allowed to pass. Willett!"

"Yes, sir."

"How many men do we have?"

"About 750."

"That's one of us for every two of them."

"What about this . . . Nicholas Herkimer?" Mellon asked.

Robby suddenly snapped to attention.

"Herkimer left Fort Dayton two days ago," Gansevoort said, "with his Tryon County militia. He's got about eight hundred men. Chances are he won't get through."

"But that's a force as large as our own."

"They're farmers," Gansevoort countered. "Untrained. Mostly German immigrants. The only weapons they have are whatever they've brought from their barns and homes. I sent word four days ago asking them for help. I *hope* they get through. We need them."

Willett spoke up. "I'm worried less about our numbers than I am about our morale."

"What do you mean?" Gansevoort asked.

"I've been listening to the men. We declared independence over a year ago, and what do we have to show for it? Montgomery lost at Quebec. Sullivan lost at Flatbush. Burgoyne holds Ticonderoga. Washington spends most of his time retreating through the Jerseys. We can count, maybe, two minor victories—Washington capturing Trenton last Christmas Eve, and his beating Cornwallis's rear guard after most of the British army had already left Princeton. Our money's worthless. We can hardly buy supplies, and speculators are getting rich selling to our enemies."

Gansevoort cut in. "But things are coming our way too, Marinus. We ran the British out of Boston to start the war, don't forget. And the colonies are coming together. Pennsylvania, New Jersey, and all of New England are behind us now, and so is Georgia. Maryland may be a little shaky, but she'll come around. And when our people hear that Johnny Johnson's coming back, thinking to recover his riches, they'll get their morale up all right!"

Corporal Manning stepped in. "St. Leger doesn't think so, sir. He thinks the valley will rally round Johnson and turn against us. Rumor has it he wrote Burgoyne that he'd take us without a shot being fired and that they'd meet as victors in Albany. He thinks we'll fold, sir."

They were silent for a moment. Then Mellon spoke up. "Colonel Gansevoort," he said, "may I make a suggestion?"

Gansevoort looked at him.

"May I suggest we raise a flag?"

"A flag?"

"Yes. It would at least let the British know they've got a fight on their hands, and I believe it would boost the men's morale—inspire them—remind them there's something to fight for."

"But we haven't got a flag."

"We can *make* one."

Mellon reached into his pocket and pulled out a folded document.

"I brought with me a copy of a resolution passed by Congress on June 14, less than two months ago. It states what our flag shall be. It says, 'Thirteen stripes alternating red and white. And in the upper corner on a field of deep blue, thirteen white stars, representing a new constellation.' " He handed the document to Gansevoort. "People call it 'Old Glory.'"[5]

" 'Thirteen stripes alternating . . .' Where's a quill?" Someone handed one to Gansevoort, and he gave it to Mellon. "Draw it."

"Well, I've never actually seen it, sir, but I'll try."

"I'll draw it!" The sudden outburst from Robby's dark corner startled them. Robby jumped to his feet and ran to the table. "Let me draw it, sir," he repeated. "I've seen it."

Gansevoort looked at the other men, shrugged his shoulders, then handed Robby the quill and a sheet of paper.

"Golly," Robby said, inspecting the quill. "This is neat!"

"The flag, boy. Draw the *flag!*"

Robby dipped the quill in the ink and began to draw.

"The stripes go like this." He made bold strokes horizontally across the paper. "Red, white, red, white, red, white, and so on. Thirteen of them, you see? The field of blue is in *this* corner." He inked the quill again. "And the stars are arranged . . . like this . . . in a circle." He handed the drawing to Gansevoort.

Gansevoort studied it. "Thirteen stripes . . . field of blue . . . Yes! . . . Splendid!" He slapped the table with his hand. "Oh, will that vex the British! They'll go to bed tonight figuring we'll fold, and next morning we'll greet them with Old Glory flying in their faces." He laughed. "Corporal Manning, get Molly Winder." Molly Winder had a well-deserved reputation as a skilled seamstress.

Corporal Manning left the room.

"And Willett," Gansevoort continued, "get Abraham Swartout. His quarters are just outside."

Willett left and returned a moment later with a tall soldier.

"Swartout," Gansevoort said. "Didn't you capture a blue coat from the British at Peekskill?"

"I did, sir."

"I have a proposition for you. Our new flag, Old Glory, needs a rich fabric for a star-specked field of deep blue. I invite your coat to volunteer itself for that service."

Abraham Swartout, sensing instantly what was afoot, bowed deeply. "My coat, sir, would be honored."[6]

Swartout went to fetch his coat as the others cleared the table. He returned a moment later, coat in hand, followed shortly thereafter by Corporal Manning and Molly Winder. Tagging behind Molly was a young Indian girl who looked to be about fifteen years old.

"Molly!" Gansevoort said energetically, his eyes dancing. "We're going to make a flag, and we need your help. Abraham Swartout's coat will give us the blue we need. Now we need some white fabric to make stars and stripes and some red fabric for another set of stripes. What have you got?"

"Let's see," Molly thought. "For white we can use ammunition shirts. We've got plenty of them." She turned to the young Indian girl. "White Fawn, you know where the ammunition shirts are. Go fetch some."

White Fawn nodded and left.

"Now, we need red," Molly said thoughtfully as Gansevoort stroked his chin and the other soldiers looked uncertainly about the room.

Suddenly Molly's face brightened. "I know just

the thing!"

With an exaggerated upper-class air, she curtsied and said, "Pardon me, gentlemen." She bent over slightly, grasped her floor-length dress with both hands just below the knees and straightened up, raising the hem of her dress about a foot off the floor.

"My red flannel petticoat!" she said.[7]

The men laughed delightedly at that, and some of them applauded. Gansevoort said, "Perfect!" then motioned to the men. "Circle around Molly, gentlemen, faces out. We'll form a shield for the delicacies."

Hidden within the circle of men, Molly removed the petticoat. Stepping from the circle, she laid it on the table next to Abraham Swartout's blue coat. White Fawn returned a moment later with the ammunition shirts.

"All right," Gansevoort said. "We've got our red, white, and blue. Let's begin."

As they began to work around the table, their spirits high, Robby saw an opportunity.

"Indian girl!" he said in a stage whisper. "Indian girl! Come here!"

White Fawn drew near. "My name is White Fawn," she said.

Robby spoke to her in quiet-but-urgent tones. "I've got to find Nicholas Herkimer. Do you know him? They said he's about ten miles away, coming up the south side of the Mohawk River. Can you tell me how to get there?"

"Who are *you?*"

He put his finger to his lips. "Shh! . . . I'm Robby Barton. I've got to get to the south side of the Mohawk

River."

"You'll never make it by yourself, Robby." She was whispering now, her face close to his. "It's dark out there, and the British are camped all around the fort. You'll either get lost or get caught. I think you should stay here."

"But I've *got* to find him," Robby said, desperation showing in his voice. "I've got a message for him from Benjamin Franklin. It's *very* important."

White Fawn looked at him. He looked back at her. She sighed; he sighed. After a moment, she smiled. He relaxed, then smiled back. "Come on," she said. "You'd never make it by yourself. I'll show you the way."

"All *right!*"

White Fawn grabbed Robby's hand. "Let's go," she said, and together they slipped out of the fort and into the night.

10:45 p.m. At the headquarters camp of General Barry St. Leger, British soldiers were sleeping around a dying campfire. The general himself slept in a large tent set fifty feet deeper into the woods. The night was quiet except for hooting owls, chirping crickets, and vigorous snoring in several pitches and tempos. Then came another sound—the sound of two protesting young voices—faint at first, but growing louder. Before long, Robby and White Fawn stumbled into the camp, pushed unceremoniously by a sentry carrying a musket. A woman trailed behind with a hard look and a dress guaranteed to draw soldiers' stares. The soldiers around the campfire began to stir.

"Get General St. Leger!" the sentry said.

One of the soldiers got to his feet, shuffled sleepily to the door of the general's tent, and spoke through the fabric. After a moment, St. Leger[8] emerged, blinking his eyes and running both hands through his hair, obviously displeased.

"What's going on?" he bellowed as he approached his men.

The sentry said, "This woman came up to me and said there's a large body of men heading toward Fort Stanwix, and then, when we were coming to see you, we found these children trying to sneak across our lines."

St. Leger looked warily at Robby and White Fawn. "We haven't got time for children. Let them go. . . . No! They could cause us trouble. Tie them to that tree. Let them be comfortable, but make sure they're secure. We'll have someone take them out of here in the morning."

The sentry and the woman dragged Robby and White Fawn to opposite sides of a large tree. Pulling their arms forward around the tree, they cuffed them wrist to wrist with lengths of rope, leaving slack so they could sit down. After securing the knots, they returned to where the general stood.

"Now," St. Leger said to the sentry, "what about the woman?"

"She says there's a large body of men heading from Fort Dayton to Fort Stanwix to reinforce the rebels."

St. Leger looked the woman over, a scowl on his face. "Why should we believe her. She looks like a hard one. It could be a trap."

"She says get John Johnson. He'll vouch for her."

St. Leger yelled toward his tent. "Johnson! Brant! Get out here!"

Two men emerged from the tent—a striking Indian about thirty-five years old with a regal bearing and a commanding presence,[9] and a shorter, older man, a bit pudgy and more than a bit bald, with the look of a man not to be trifled with.[10]

"Johnson," St. Leger said, "what do you know of this woman?"

Johnson looked at her, then brightened in recognition. "Mary. What are you doing here?" He turned to St. Leger. "I know her. She was my mistress."

St. Leger snorted. "And I suppose *all* your mistresses are loyal?"

"This one is, sir, I can assure you."

St. Leger turned to the woman. "Tell me what you know."

"Well, sir, Nicholas Herkimer sent word throughout the valley that every able-bodied man from sixteen to sixty was to join the militia on a march to Fort Stanwix to help the rebels fight against you, sir.[11] They met day before yesterday at Fort Dayton, at the mouth of West Canada Creek. They're marching up the south side of the Mohawk, and they're camped for the night a ways below Oriskany Creek. They'll reach here tomorrow morning. There must be close to a thousand of them."

"Are they well armed?"

"They have arms, sir, at least some of them do. But they don't march like soldiers. They're just farmers, and they're not very organized. A few have horses, and there's some wagons, but mostly they're just sort of hiking toward the fort, not in any military way.

They'll be more cautious when they get here, but if you meet them early, it shouldn't be hard to catch them off guard."

Brant, the Indian, spoke. "To get past Oriskany Creek they'll have to drop into a ravine that's about ten or twelve rods across. We could position ourselves around it during the night, ambush them as they cross, and stop them before they knew what hit them."

St. Leger thought for a moment. "All right. Johnson, you take your Royal Yorkers. And go wake up John Butler. He can take his Tory Rangers." He turned to the Indian. "Brant, you know the country, so you lead the way with your braves. You sure you can organize the men and be in place by morning?"

"We can."

"Good. All of you together will make a force equal to theirs, but you're superior soldiers, and you'll have surprise on your side. Finish the job in a hurry. I'd like to lay siege to Fort Stanwix tomorrow if we can, and I don't want my troops exhausted from a long battle."

Johnson and Brant nodded agreement.

"Now, organize yourselves and be on your way. It's in your hands. I'm going back to bed."

The general returned to his tent, and Johnson and Brant left to arouse their troops. The men around the campfire settled again into their sleeping gear, and before long the sounds of snoring returned.

At the tree, Robby and White Fawn remained alert, scarcely daring to breathe. Finally, Robby spoke in hushed tones. "We've got to get to Nicholas Herkimer. They'll *kill* him. We need to *warn* him, and I promised Ben I'd give him his message."

"Scrunch one of your hands down real tiny," White Fawn said. "I'll try to slip the rope over it."

She worked one-handedly at that until Robby's hand was rough and red, then she sank back and shook her head, disheartened. "It's too tight."

They sat, dispirited, thinking.

"I know!" White Fawn said brightening. "Let's pull the rope back and forth against the tree, like this. Maybe we can wear it through."

"But that would take *forever*."

Her brightness faded. "I know."

They sat in silence again.

Finally White Fawn said. "Then we'll just have to untie one of the knots. I don't see how we can do it one-handed, but we've got four knots to work on. Maybe one of them's loose enough to come free. I'll work on your knots, and you work on mine. . . . Robby, do you ever pray?"

"Yes . . . sometimes."

"I think we'd better pray now." They bowed their heads, and White Fawn spoke the words. When she concluded, they stretched their arms toward each other and grasped hands for brief moment. Then awkwardly, determinedly, they began their assault against the knots.

August 6, 1777

5:45 a.m. About a mile from Fort Stanwix, on a line from the fort to Oriskany Creek, the first rays of morning sunlight colored a meadow that sat atop a gentle knoll. The meadow was small—no more than fifty feet across. Grass and wildflowers filled it, and dense forest surrounded it on all sides. The parapets of Fort Stanwix were visible to the northwest. Robby and White Fawn burst suddenly into the meadow. Robby stumbled and collapsed in a heap.

"Wait, wait! I've got to rest," he said panting. "I'm not used to running like this. . . . And I don't know how you can even *see*."

"It's getting lighter, Robby, and we won't get there if we don't run. I guess we can rest for a moment, but then we've got to go."

White Fawn sat beside Robby while he caught his breath.

"White Fawn, what will we do when we get there? I mean, can we get past the ravine without St. Leger's men spotting us?"

"We can go above it. They'll be clustered near the deepest part of the ravine, close to the river. That's where the farmers will go. Higher up, the underbrush gets so thick it'd slow down a large group of men. But we're small, and there's only two of us, so we can go through it. We'll circle around St. Leger's men, and drop down to where the farmers will have to pass. Once we warn them, they can ambush the soldiers, instead of the other way around." She stood. "We've got to go now. With the sun coming up, the farmers'll be breaking camp. I don't know how far they've got to hike to reach the creek, but if we don't hurry, they'll get there before we do. Come on!"

Robby stood, glancing back toward the fort. Suddenly his breath caught in his chest. "White Fawn," he exclaimed. "Look!"

She turned toward the fort.

"Look at Fort Stanwix!" Robby cried. "They're raising Old Glory. They finished the flag last night, and now they're raising it. . . . And look. The wind must've picked up all of a sudden. Look how the flag flies straight out! And the men are cheering. Do you hear them? Hooray for Old Glory!"

Robby hugged White Fawn, and she hugged him back. "Hooray!" Robby shouted again. Then White Fawn said, "Come on. We've got to go."

With a final glance at Old Glory, they put their backs to the fort and ran into the forest again.

Robby and White Fawn approached the ravine slowly, their nerves bristling. A somber, graying sky now darkened the forest with thickening shadows and a threat of rain. They crept stealthily, peering into the trees, wriggling mostly through obstinate thicket, scampering now and then as the thicket cleared—brambles tearing at them, branches springing back in their wake, leaves crunching menacingly beneath their feet. Suddenly, a short distance away, shots rang out—slowly at first, then with ever-increasing fury.[12]

"No!" Robby cried. "We're too late! They're ambushing the farmers!"

He spun around, desperate.

"What am I going to do? I've got to give Nicholas Herkimer Ben's message!"

He began to run, pushing the underbrush aside. White Fawn ran after him and in about fifteen feet caught him, her momentum throwing both of them to the ground.

"No, Robby! There's nothing we can do now. If you run into the ambush, all you'll do is get yourself killed. If the farmers win, you can give Herkimer your message. If they lose, you did the best you could."

"But I promised Ben! And I still don't know the answer to my question."

"*Robby!*" White Fawn said emphatically. "There's nothing more you can do!"

They sat, despondent. The sounds of fighting overwhelmed them. Then thunder roared and rain began to fall. The sounds of fighting diminished, then finally came to a stop.

"It's over," Robby said, as tears formed in his eyes.

White Fawn suddenly looked up. "Robby! It's not over! They've just had to stop fighting. They can't fire their muskets in the rain because the powder gets wet. They *always* stop when it rains, then start fighting again when it dries out."[13] She stood and pulled Robby to his feet. "If it keeps raining, we may get through. We'll be harder to see in the rain, and we won't have to be as quiet. Besides, I know how to get through. This is my playground. I grew up here! *Come on!*"

Nicholas Herkimer's horse had been killed in the first volley. Nicholas himself was wounded in the left leg, leaving it useless. He'd had his saddle removed from his horse, and now he sat on it, his back against a tree.

"Get the men organized," he said to an aide. "Have them close in and form a perimeter while we've got a chance."

A voice from a short distance away shouted, "Who goes there?"

A second voice said, "Wait, I see them. They're only children—a boy . . . and an Indian girl."

Now Robby's voice carried above the rain. "We've got to find Nicholas Herkimer. Do you know where he is?"

The second voice said, "Come. I'll take you to him."

The children approached the tree where Nicholas Herkimer sat. Robby dropped to his knees beside him.

"Are you Nicholas Herkimer?"

"Yes. I'm Nicholas Herkimer. Who are you, and where did you come from?"

"I'm Robby Barton, and this is White Fawn. We came from Fort Stanwix, and then we got caught by General St. Leger. We heard them plan to ambush you, and tried to warn you, but we were too late. When it started to rain, we thought maybe we could sneak by the redcoats, and we did."

"Tell me, son. We've heard Johnny Johnson's leading a band of Tories. Is he here?"

"Yes, and so's Joseph Brant, the Indian."

Herkimer sighed. "My brother is one of Johnny Johnson's captains.[14] He may even be here now. Oh, what bitter feelings this war has brought among family and friends!"

He looked to the sky. A scowl drew across his face as he turned to his aide. "The rain's stopping. They'll be firing before long. Tell the men to be on the alert. If we have to break ranks, have them move high into the underbrush. Make the enemy come in low."

Robby pointed to Herkimer's leg. "You're injured."

Herkimer laughed in a self-deprecating sort of way. "Yes. The great Nicholas Herkimer didn't last long. My horse got shot out from under me in the first volley, and *I* got shot in the leg."[15]

Herkimer craned his neck and looked right and left into the forest. "It won't be long now. . . . Confound it, where's Schmidt? Schmidt! Come here! Quickly!"

A large farmer appeared suddenly from behind the tree.

Herkimer turned to Robby and White Fawn. "I'll have Schmidt take you out. He knows where the enemy's the thickest, and he should be able to get you back through the lines. Thank you both for coming. You did your best, but we all seem to be a little late today."

Robby tried to protest. "No, wait!" Herkimer cut him off.

"Schmidt, take the boy and the girl and get them out of here. I won't have children dying with us."

"Yes, sir!"

Schmidt grabbed both children by the arm and drew them to their feet.

"Wait!" Robby said. "I can't go yet!"

"Get them out of here!" Herkimer shouted.

Schmidt looped his arms around both children and lifted them off their feet.

Suddenly Robby's voice rang clear and true above

the preparations for battle: *"I've got a message from Benjamin Franklin!"*

Herkimer looked up, a stunned expression on his face. "Schmidt! Let them go."

Schmidt put the children down. They knelt beside Herkimer again.

"What do you mean?" Herkimer said.

"I'm Benjamin Franklin's messenger. He sent me to you."

"He sent *you* . . . to *me?*"

"Yes. But I *wanted* to come because I've got to ask you a question. Ben said that you and he were best friends, and that you used to talk all the time, and that I should ask you—"

"Best friends? Don't be ridiculous. I've never met Benjamin Franklin. Now, where's the message? We haven't got have much time."

Robby stared at him. "But . . ."

"Do you have a message or don't you?"

Robby's shoulders slumped. He reached inside his linen shirt, drew out an envelope, and gave it to Herkimer, who opened it, pulled out a sheet of paper, and began to read.

" 'Paris, France, August 6, 1777 . . .' How can that be? That's today. You can't get a message from Paris to here in a day."

"I tell you, sir, it's *true!*"

Herkimer stared at Robby. Clear, purposeful eyes stared back. Herkimer felt his misgivings waver, then weaken, then die, vanquished by an odd sensation of peace. He released his breath and shook his head. "I don't know why," he said softly, "but for some reason I believe you."

Resolute now, he turned to the message again.

> *Paris, France*
> *August 6, 1777*
>
> *My dear friend Nicholas,*
>
> > *Red petticoats fly over*
> *Fort Stanwix.*
>
> > *Your friend, Ben.*

Herkimer looked at Robby. "That's *it?* That's the message? 'Red petticoats fly over Fort Stanwix'?"

Robby jumped to his feet, the words pouring out in a rush. "Yes, sir! I know what it means. He's talking about the flag. I heard Colonel Gansevoort and the others talking yesterday in Fort Stanwix. They were worried about morale because they haven't seen many victories, yet they have to stop St. Leger or the war will probably be lost. Colonel Mellon had a resolution from Congress that told them how to make a flag with red and white stripes and thirteen stars on a blue field, so they said let's make a flag and fly it in the faces of the British. Captain Swartout gave them his blue coat, and they had ammunition shirts for white, but they didn't know where to get red cloth. And that's when Molly Winder pulled up the hem of her dress and said they could use her red flannel petticoat, and they made the flag out of it. 'Red petticoats fly over Fort Stanwix' means that the *American flag* is flying over Fort Stanwix, and it's true! We saw it! Old Glory is flying over Fort Stanwix! *The Americans are going to win!*"

For a moment Nicholas Herkimer said nothing. Nearby a shot rang out. Then another. A broad smile grew on Nicholas Herkimer's face. "Hah!" he said.

"Maybe we weren't so late after all."

He drew Robby into his chest and hugged him. The shots were picking up. He grabbed White Fawn and hugged her too. "Now go on. Get out of here. We've got some fighting to do!"

Robby moved toward Schmidt, who waited to take the two of them away, but White Fawn stood firm.

"No!" she said, grabbing Nicholas Herkimer's musket that stood propped against the tree. "I can shoot a musket better than any man. I'm staying here, sir—by you. I won't go."

Robby stepped forward. "Let her stay, sir. I *know* she can fight, but I've got to go. Ben said to go home as soon as I left the message. Otherwise I'd stay too."

Nicholas Herkimer smiled. "I understand, son. Now be gone."

All around them the firing continued to increase. Robby drew himself tall and saluted. "Goodbye, General Herkimer."

General Herkimer saluted back. "Goodbye, Robby."

Robby stepped to White Fawn and hugged her. "Goodbye, White Fawn. And thank you."

"Goodbye, Robby."

Robby hesitated a moment longer, then turned to Schmidt and said, "Let's go."

Schmidt led Robby into the forest. White Fawn raised her hand and waved. Then she turned back to Herkimer, knelt on one knee beside him, and loaded the musket.

The sounds of battle were reaching a peak. General Herkimer shouted commands to his troops. Screams of agony punctuated a background of guttural cursing by men locked in hand-to-hand combat.

Her musket now loaded, White Fawn took a breath to steady herself. Then she peered into the battle zone, raised the musket to her shoulder, and fired.[16]

April 18, 1990

5:45 a.m. Ben let Robby sleep until it was almost time to get up. Then he approached Robby's bedside and once again shook him gently. Robby opened his eyes.

"Oh, Ben!" he said sitting up. "I'm so glad you're here. I went to Fort Stanwix, and I got captured by General St. Leger, and we wouldn't have found Nicholas Herkimer except it rained, and—"

" I *know*, Robby. You did a wonderful job."

Robby scooted himself to one side of the bed, and Ben sat down.

"Ben?"

"Yes, Robby?"

"What happened to General Herkimer?"

"He died . . . but not during the battle. Ten days later. At home."[17]

"What about White Fawn?"

"She died too."

Robby's shoulders drooped. "Oh . . ."

Ben laughed. "When she was forty-seven! She took care of herself, she did. She really could shoot a musket better than any man, just as she said."

"Oh, that's wonderful! But, Ben . . ."

"Yes, Robby?"

"Nicholas Herkimer said he'd never met you. But *you* said you were good friends and that you used to talk all the time."

"Ah, yes. But that was afterward."

"Afterward?"

"Yes. Afterward. After he died. And after I died too, of course. Then we had plenty of time to talk. And plenty to talk about too."

Robby was silent for a moment.

"He liked your message, Ben."

"I knew he would. You see, he thought he'd failed. He *died* thinking he'd failed. But he didn't fail. Nicholas and his farmers fought for six hours there at Oriskany Creek, and for all six hours Nicholas sat on his saddle directing his troops with White Fawn by his side. Eventually the enemy gave up and ran back to St. Leger, but by then they were so demoralized they didn't want to fight anymore. So St. Leger sat around Fort Stanwix for eighteen days, trying to rally his troops, but he finally gave up and retreated. Thanks to Nicholas and his men, St. Leger never made it through the Mohawk Valley, so Burgoyne had to fight on his own, and we beat him. That's what turned the war around. My friend Nicholas Herkimer turned the war around."[18]

"Wow!" Robby said.

"But Nicholas didn't know it. When he died ten days after the battle, St. Leger and his troops still surrounded the fort. As far as Nicholas knew, the patriots had lost, and he'd failed to do what he set out to do. Thinking he'd failed pained him more than the bungled amputation that killed him, and it kept him from comforting his family as they went through those last ten days with him. *That,* he told me, was the greatest pain of all—knowing that he'd failed to comfort his family." Ben put his hand gently on Robby's shoulder. "That's your dad's greatest pain too, Robby."

Robby's eyes narrowed for a moment, then widened again as he understood.

"My dad thinks he's failed . . . and that's why he hasn't been comforting us."

"That's right. But the only reason he thinks he's failed is because he doesn't see the whole picture, just as Nicholas Herkimer didn't see the whole picture. Mortals *never* see the whole picture, Robby. That's why you have to have faith."

Robby nodded, beginning to see.

"You know, the first time I met Nicholas I was so excited. To me he was one of the great heroes of the revolution. After we got to be such very good friends, he told me how terrible he felt because he didn't have enough faith to comfort his family during those last ten days. And then I saw a way to help him, and that's why I came to you."

"So I could give him your message."

"Yes, so you could give him my message. You see, when I was very old, I had a sort of whimsical idea. I thought, wouldn't it be wonderful if life were like a book.[19] Then we could all write second editions and correct a few of the errors we'd made in the first. Well, when Nicholas told me about those last ten days of his life, that idea came back to me. So I thought about it, came up with a plan—a way Nicholas could write a second edition of those last ten days—and the Council approved it. And you were the most important part of the plan. I really appreciate your help, Robby. I couldn't have done it without you."

"But Ben, you said I could ask Nicholas about freedom, but I never got to. The rain was stopping, and people were getting their muskets dried out, and everyone was starting to fire again, and it was all happening so fast I never had a chance."

"But you got your answer, didn't you?"

Robby hesitated. "I don't think so."

"You got your answer, Robby. You saw it flying in the wind over Fort Stanwix."

"Old Glory?"

"Red petticoats, Robby. Red petticoats flying over Fort Stanwix. That's your answer. My message to Nicholas was also my message to *you*."

"I don't understand."

"Robby, what could be more ordinary than a red flannel petticoat? And yet, the last time you saw that red flannel petticoat, what was it doing?"

"It was flying over Fort Stanwix."

"That ordinary red flannel petticoat became Old Glory, Robby, and that's how we are. We're just ordinary people, as ordinary as red flannel petticoats. But if we look deep, deep inside, we can see Old Glory flying there. What you saw flying above Fort Stanwix was *us*—ordinary people flying as high as Old Glory—because sometimes that's what we have to do. You see, Robby, when ordinary people come together, they can make great things happen. You not only saw it, Robby, you were *part* of it."

Robby reflected. "Red petticoats flying over Fort Stanwix. . . . Ordinary people doing great things!"

"That's right, Robby. But there's something else you must see—something *very* important. Before that red flannel petticoat could become Old Glory, something had to happen to it. Can you think what it was?"

Robby thought about it. "I don't know."

"You *do* know, Robby. Think about it again."

Robby closed his eyes. *Molly Winder lifted up the*

hem of her dress, and the men backed into a circle around her so she could take off her petticoat. She put the petticoat on the table, and White Fawn brought in the ammunition shirts. And then Molly took her scissors, and . . . "I know! It had to get cut up!"

"That's right, Robby. Before that red petticoat could fly as part of Old Glory, it had to get cut up. And sometimes, before *we* can fly, parts of us—parts of life we've known and grown comfortable with—may also have to get cut up."

A dawning began to glow in Robby's heart. "You mean . . . like losing a job?"

"Yes, Robby. Like losing a job. Where I live now, we call those sorts of things 'assignments,' because you learn from them. That's their purpose. But unless you have faith, assignments can seem terrible and unfair. Your father's got a tough assignment, Robby, and he's struggling with it. But so are you, and that's also part of the way things work."

"What do you mean?"

"Even the best red flannel petticoat can't become Old Glory on its own."

"That's *right*. It had to join Abraham Swartout's coat and the ammunition shirts."

"Which means?"

"That the reason we can fly is because we don't do it alone—we fly together!"

"And when we at last discover that we ordinary people can fly as high as Old Glory if we work together, how do we feel?"

"Free! We feel free!"

"Yes. Now you understand."

"So . . . that's why those people knocked down the Berlin Wall."

"That's right, Robby. Their government assumed they couldn't fly, but people won't be held down forever. We knew that, Robby. That's why we wrote the United States Constitution the way we did."

"*You* wrote the Constitution?"

"I helped."

"Boy, that must've been hard."

"Well . . . I suppose it was. But do you know what the worst part was?"

"What?"

Ben smiled. "No air conditioning!"

"Really?"

"No, Robby. It *was* a long, hot summer, but the hardest part was figuring out who to give the power to. That's what we were doing, you see."

"You were giving people *power?*"

"That's how *we* saw it. When we beat the British, we won the power to govern. When we wrote the Constitution, we were just giving it out again.

"So who did you give it to?"

"We gave some of it to the national government, and some of it we gave to the states. But most of it we kept where it belongs—with the people. You see, Robby, the power to govern is a God-given right of ordinary people like you and me."

Robby smiled. "Red flannel petticoats."

"Yes, Robby. Red flannel petticoats. And the only way we could protect the power of ordinary people was to require that they be responsible. They're the same thing, you know—responsibility and power. You see, if we give away our responsibility . . . "

". . . we give away our power!"

"Yes. And we end up with the same thing we fought the British over—a government with more power than it can wisely handle. Now, does that answer your question?"

"Oh, yes, Ben! It does!"

"Now, Robby, you got your answer because you were willing to accept a very difficult assignment. Will you accept another one?"

Robby hesitated only a moment, then nodded firmly. "Yes, Ben. I will."

"Good. This is the assignment. Honor what you have learned. Share with your friends what it means to be free. *Show* them what it means by your example. But you must never mention meeting me, and you must never mention your wonderful adventure at Fort Stanwix—except on one occasion. On that occasion you will again become my messenger. You will tell someone of your adventure, and you will offer that person an opportunity to learn as you have learned. When the time to deliver that message comes, I'll let you know. Do you understand?"

"Yes, Ben. I understand."

"Good." Ben stood to go. "You know, Robby, I got up one day in the middle of our Constitutional Convention and said, 'The longer I live, the more convincing proofs I see of this truth, that God governs in the affairs of men.'[20] And then I encouraged everyone to pray so that we could put aside our differences and work together and write the Constitution well. When we finished, people called it a miracle. I can tell you now, Robby, it *was* a miracle."

Robby stood and wrapped his arms around Ben.

"Oh, thank you, Ben! Thank you!"

They hugged for a moment. When they separated, Ben put his hands on Robby's shoulders and smiled gently. "You were a good messenger, Robby. I spoke with Nicholas before I left, and he said to tell you hello and to let you know that he appreciates what you did. I also spoke with White Fawn." Ben paused, his smile broadening.

"And . . . ?"

Ben hugged Robby again. "And White Fawn sends her love."

9:04 a.m. "Robby," Mrs. Elliott said. "Would you lead us in the Pledge of Allegiance?"

Robby gave Mrs. Elliott an ear-to-ear grin, then walked to the corner of the room where the flagpole stood. He carried it to the center of the room, took a step back, and placed his hand over his heart. Then his eyes opened wider, and his mouth dropped. He stepped to the flag again and lifted it to reveal what lay hidden within the folds.

"This is it! This is it!"

"What is it, Robby?"

"This is the flag that flew over Fort Stanwix. This is red flannel petticoats—red petticoats flying over Fort Stanwix."

Mrs. Elliott smiled, pleasantly surprised. "I didn't think any of you would know that story. Did your parents tell you about Fort Stanwix, Robby?"

"But this is the *real flag*. I've seen it. Where did you get it?"

"It's not the *real* flag, Robby. I helped *make* this flag when I was in sixth grade. Our teacher, Mr.

Harding, told us about Nicholas Herkimer and the Battle of Oriskany and how the soldiers at Fort Stanwix flew a flag they'd made from a red flannel petticoat. Then he helped us make one just like it. We got a blue blanket and some white sheets, and he bought us some red flannel at the store. We said our pledge to Old Glory for the rest of the year."

Robby still looked uncertain. "But why is it here?"

"After class yesterday, when I was preparing for our discussion on freedom, I remembered the story of Nicholas Herkimer and how much it had inspired me when I was a child. So I called Mr. Harding and asked him if he would come and tell *our* class the story, and he said he would. He'd even kept the flag we made, so he brought it with him this morning." She gestured toward the back of the room. "Mr. Harding, would you come forward so the class can see you?"

Mr. Harding stood and waved to the class. He was a kindly old gentleman with a warm smile and a familiar looking face.

"You're him!" Robby cried. "You're Ben!"

Mr. Harding laughed as he began walking toward the front of the room. "Yes I am, son. I'm Ben Harding. But I know what you mean. People tell me I look just like Benjamin Franklin, and I'm proud to think that in some small way I can be like him. Great men founded our country, my young friends, and today I'll tell you about one of the best of them—Nicholas Herkimer, the hero of the Battle of Oriskany."

"I know him, sir. He's a friend of mine."

Mr. Harding nodded. "He's a friend of all of us. He took a stand for freedom—a stand for *us*—and he turned the war around. He never knew it, but he did."

Robby stood a bit taller as he remembered. "He knows it now, sir."

Mr. Harding thought for a moment, then smiled and said, "Yes, I suppose he does. Well, I didn't mean to interrupt your pledge. Please go on. Then I'll tell you about the first flag that ever flew over an American fort, and you'll see what you're really pledging your allegiance to."

"I know, sir. Red petticoats flying over Fort Stanwix. And that's *us!*"

Robby turned to face Old Glory. Then, placing his hand again over his heart, he led his classmates in the pledge.

PART 2

Kathy

Ben and Nicholas

Mrs. Elliott hesitated near the door. Ben stepped toward her, his hand extended. "Come in, Mrs. Elliott. Please don't be nervous. We're grateful that you could come."

Mrs. Elliott smiled self-consciously. Ben took her hand and drew her toward a slightly smaller man who stood waiting within a circle of three comfortable-looking, exquisitely upholstered chairs. "This is my friend Nicholas Herkimer," Ben said.

Nicholas took her hand. "So you're Robby's teacher," he said, smiling broadly.

Mrs. Elliott nodded. She wasn't quite ready to trust her voice.

"He's a fine boy," Nicholas said. "But I'm sure you know that."

She nodded again, then Ben gestured for them all to sit.

"We're pleased you could come," Ben said again, reassuringly.

Mrs. Elliott cleared her throat, and finding it working, said, "Mr. Harding *does* look like you."

Ben laughed. "He really does! That was one of the nice features of the plan—one of the little details that seemed to fall into place. Tell me, Mrs. Elliott . . . or may I call you Kathy?"

"Please, call me Kathy."

"And call me Ben—"

"And I'm Nicholas."

"So tell me, Kathy, when Robby told you about his experience, what did you think?"

"Well"—she laughed, still nervous—"I was

surprised, but, you know, it's really funny. I believed him right away. I sort of had a *feeling* . . ."

Nicholas chuckled. "I know what you mean, Kathy. When I was sitting there on my saddle and Robby gave me Ben's note, I read the date—'August sixth'—and I read the place—'Paris, France'—and I *knew* it was all impossible. Yet, something said to me, 'This is *true!*' " He shook his head and chuckled again, remembering. "I've learned since then that we all have a certain power—even as mortals—a power of spiritual discernment that goes beyond logic." He paused. "You know Ralph Waldo Emerson, don't you?"

"Well, I don't *know* him . . ."

Nicholas laughed. "I realize that. I didn't meet him myself until I got *here*. But you've read his works, haven't you?"

"Yes, some of them."

"He once wrote, 'A breath of will blows eternally through the universe of souls in the direction of the Right and the Necessary.'[21] That 'breath of will' is what we both sensed, Kathy. It's quite a treasure, actually, our ability to do that."

"And it's a compliment to both of *you* that you honored it," Ben said. "Too many mortals discount whatever they can't understand."

"I think I was open to believing," Kathy said, "because I saw the change that came over Robby. He was so *transformed,* and there had to be *some* explanation for it. His father and mother have changed so much too. Robby told me they got the kids together for a family meeting, then told them *exactly* how things stood and how it was a great opportunity to do whatever they wanted to do. So they set some family goals, and Robby

says they're working on them. They've arranged
something with the bank, apparently, and Robby says
his father's got some exciting new ideas underway.
Anyway, it wasn't hard to believe in miracles after
seeing all that. So when Robby stayed after school that
day and said he could tell me *everything,* and especially when he said I could talk with both of you if I wanted
to, *well* . . ."—she sniffled—"I don't know what to say.
It's just wonderful!" She threw up her hands, tears
brightening the corners of her eyes.

Ben smiled warmly. "We owe you something, you
know. You were part of the plan."

"I wondered what happened!" Kathy exclaimed,
wiping her eyes with the back of her hand. "We were
talking about that piece of concrete from the Berlin
Wall, and I had some simple ideas about freedom to
discuss. And then, all of a sudden, here comes this
thought into my head about people being free to lose
their jobs or their homes. It threw me for a total loop!
I had to catch my breath before I could go on. I
suppose *you* did that?"

Ben laughed. "Yes, I'm afraid I did. We operate
under very strict constraints when it comes to med-
dling in mortal affairs, but that *was* one of the things
the Council allowed me to do."

"So . . . I'm curious. What else did this . . . Council
allow you to do."

"We'll, just as you said, I put that thought into
your head—the one about people being free to lose
their jobs or their homes. Then I inspired you with a
hunch that Robby's family was in trouble. I visited
Robby that evening, of course, and asked him to
become my messenger. Old Glory was actually raised

for the first time on the *third* of August, three days before the battle, so I had to arrange to have *that* put off, until the morning of the sixth. And finally, in the original battle, Colonel Gansevoort actually sent White Fawn through the enemy lines to warn Nicholas about the ambush—that's how *skilled* she was—but I arranged to have her wait and get the idea from her experiences with Robby. I believe that's it. Oh! And then I asked Robby to talk to *you*. Everything else happened because of the character of each of the people involved—yours included, Kathy. Aside from what happened to you and Robby, the only *meaningful* change was how Nicholas spent his last ten days."

Nicholas shook his head. "I can't begin to tell you how much that meant to me. . . . I'd be embarrassed to thank Ben again, Kathy, but can you *imagine* what it means to have such friends?" Nicholas smiled affectionately at Ben, his own eyes glistening.

"Well," Ben said. "I've been rewarded by cherished friends of my own. So"—he cleared his throat—"let's get down to business. What do you say?" Ben paused a moment, then proceeded. "Kathy, we've invited you here today because you influence many lives as a teacher, and—"

"Forgive me, Ben, but another question did occur to me. Could I interrupt?"

"Of course!"

"You spoke about a Council that allowed you to do the things you did. I would have expected that to have been . . . *God*."

"Well, the Council acts *for* God. God delegates, you see, and challenging assignments don't end when you die. Does that help you understand?"

Kathy reflected. "So, did you devise your plan for Robby because it was your *assignment?*"

"No, not exactly. You see, we're expected to do good of our own accord, with whatever *present* capacities we have. What we call 'assignments' are usually a step *beyond* our present capacities—things we wouldn't *conceive* of doing on our own because we don't have the wisdom for them. My plan was simply an idea that occurred to me in the normal course of seeking to use my present capacities, and the Council that has charge of those matters was kind enough to approve. My *assignments?* Well, they're a bit more challenging—beyond me, actually. But not for long. I accept them eagerly, you see."

"I do see. Thank you, Ben. Now, you were suggesting that we get down to business . . ."

Ben cleared his throat again, and with a sobering expression looked Kathy Elliott squarely in the eyes. "Kathy, because you influence people, Nicholas and I want you to fully understand the principles we're concerned about here—assuming *you* desire to understand them as well."

Kathy took this to be a question and nodded.

"From our perspective, the American culture has gotten itself off on the wrong track. We—Nicholas and I—were more fortunate in our day. We were blessed by facing a *national assignment* so trying that we *had* to clarify our values. Our times *required* that we seek and face the truth. But the mortals of your day have suffered from such prolonged temporal success that, for the most part, they've forgotten what it means to truly and wholeheartedly accept a difficult assignment, although America is, in fact, in the middle of one. In general, the people of your day mistakenly assume either that their own wisdom will suffice to guarantee success or that they're somehow *entitled* to success."[22]

"Or they accept technological success as a substitute for spiritual success," Nicholas interjected.

"Yes. Actually, there are a *number* of ways to go astray, all of them complicated, whereas the wise path is far simpler—the 'straight and narrow,' as we call it here. Our mission is to teach this simpler path. We want to clarify for you any uncertainties you may have about the principles involved. You see yourself as merely the teacher of twenty-seven sixth graders. *We* see you as the caretaker of a precious and fertile garden. The seeds you plant in those sixth-grade hearts and minds—if they are seeds of *true wisdom*—will one day nourish a nation. So we are willing to teach you if *you* are willing to learn. I must warn you, however, that if you accept this *assignment*—that's what it is, you see—you may never mention that you discussed these principles with us—that would actually work to your *dis*advantage—and you may expect to be roundly condemned by people who find that the principles take their power away. Will you accept?"

"I will," Kathy said soberly.

"Good." Ben turned to Nicholas. "How shall we proceed?"

"Why don't we let Kathy ask whatever questions she'd like? We can bring in additional topics as they occur to us."

"Fine," said Ben. "Kathy, what would you like to know?"

"Oh, my goodness!" she said. "Where should I begin?" She shifted in her chair and smoothed her skirt. "Okay, let's begin at the beginning. Is there some most basic principle that I should understand, and if so, what is it?

"I would say this," Ben answered, "that our ultimate success in *any* phase of our existence depends mainly upon two things: first, what we come to understand about who we are and what we're capable of, and, second, how we view the challenges we face. Simply put, we succeed by seeing the true nature of our existence. Would you agree, Nicholas?"

"I agree, Ben, except I would add this: the principle also applies to governments. In other words, the ultimate success of any *government* depends upon how people view their government, and how those who govern view the people they lead. Governments succeed, as people succeed, by seeing the truth about the nature of mortals and mortal life."

"Excellent point, Nicholas. As you can see, Kathy, it's really the same principle applied at two different levels—personal and political. Perhaps we could discuss the personal first, then touch on the political as we conclude. Would that be acceptable, Kathy?"

"Certainly."

"All right. Now, speaking more personally, Kathy, what is the truth—about *you?*"

As Ben asked the question, a single clear thought entered Kathy's mind. She felt a tingle of truth rise and spread within her to become an enveloping radiance. Then a more sobering thought entered her mind, and the feeling subsided as quickly as it had come. She sighed and gently shook her head.

"I see what you mean about being roundly condemned," she said.

Ben and Nicholas nodded in understanding.

"If I taught my sixth graders *that* truth," she said, "I'd probably get kicked out of school."

Ben repeated the question. "What *is* the truth about you, Kathy?"

She looked across the circle at Ben and Nicholas, the radiance filling her again. "The truth is, I am a child of God. I've known that—but I never really *understood* it before."

"Perhaps you can't teach your sixth graders that truth directly," Ben said, "but can you teach them about someone like . . . oh, who could we suggest, Nicholas?"

"I might suggest Marcus Aurelius," Nicholas answered. "I'm sure you know, Kathy, that Marcus Aurelius was a Roman emperor and one of the wisest leaders of all times. I used to read Marcus Aurelius when I was your students' age, and I can't say that I was harmed by it. Quite the contrary. The translations of his works are rather archaic, but with a little explaining they become clear enough. Listen to what Marcus Aurelius wrote: 'Thou must now at last perceive of what universe thou art a part, and of what *administrator of the universe* thy existence is an efflux, and that a limit of time is fixed for thee, which if thou dost not use for clearing away the clouds from thy mind, it will go and thou wilt go, and it will never return.' "[23] Nicholas paused to let the meaning settle in. "That 'administrator of the universe,'—of whom we are an 'efflux,' or an outflowing—is God. Can you teach your students about a man like Marcus Aurelius?"

"I believe I could."

"Or can you teach them about Helen Keller?" Ben asked. "Can you teach your sixth graders in Helen Keller's own words how *she* explained *her* greatness—how a young girl who could neither hear nor see managed to become one of the world's truly great people?"

Kathy's eyes became animated. "I *do* teach them about Helen Keller, and they *love* it! I show them *The Miracle Worker* every year. Helen Keller is my inspiration! Do you suppose—I mean, I would love—"

Ben and Nicholas stood. "Kathy," Ben said, "I'd like you to meet Helen Keller."

Helen Keller

She had seemed to simply appear. Tears formed in Kathy's eyes. Helen extended her hand. Kathy grasped it. Helen drew her into an embrace, then held her at arm's length. "You look lovely," Helen said.

"You can see!"

"But of course I can see, my dear! That shouldn't be surprising. And I can hear as well. Being without sight and hearing were simply temporary conditions. They were the core issues of my major earthly assignment, you see, and the source, therefore, of some of my most treasured wisdom, for which I am most grateful. I even agreed before I went to earth to accept a life without those two senses, although I'd forgotten that, as we all do."

"Helen, please sit here," Ben said, pulling up an extra chair. They all took their seats.

"Now, Kathy," Helen began, "Ben explained to me that you won't be allowed to refer to what I say here, so I'm going to quote from *The World I Live In,* a book I wrote in 1904: 'Faith is a mockery if it teaches us not that we may construct a world unspeakably more complete and beautiful than the material world. And I, too, may construct my better world, for *I am a child of God,* an inheritor of a fragment of the Mind that created all worlds.' "[24]

Helen sat prim and straight, watching Kathy as if measuring her response. "You see, Kathy, I sensed very deeply the truth about myself—the truth that *you* just experienced about *your* self. It was that deeply felt understanding that allowed me to do all that I did."

Kathy took a deep breath and released it. "You

know, I watch the movie they made about you—*The Miracle Worker*—and when I see the part where you're at the well, and you're fighting with your teacher about filling the pitcher with water, and then, all of a sudden, you *stop* and you grab your teacher, then drag her around the yard, wanting to know what everything is—"

"Yes," said Helen, remembering. "That's when I'd just realized that things have names."

"Every time I watch that scene, I get *goose* bumps, and tears come into my eyes, and I get all *tingly* up and down my spine. That must have been a wonderful experience!"

A rapt expression stole across Helen's face; a memory of resplendent joy animated the corners of her eyes. "It *was* a wonderful experience," she said emphatically. "A most inspiring moment. Probably the single most *thrilling* moment of my life. And it would have been denied me had I not undergone the struggle that preceded it. You see, I was searching for something, and I persisted, even though I didn't understand what I was hoping to find. I simply knew there was something I couldn't understand, somewhere I needed to go, something I needed to *be*. . . . And I persisted until I discovered it."

Ben interrupted with a gentle cough. "Kathy, I want to tell you something very special about Helen. Before she was born, when she was still nothing more than a tiny cluster of cells within her mother's womb, a single cell came into existence that was to become her brain. That single cell divided to become two, then four, then eight, then sixteen. The dividing accelerated, gathering momentum, until at its peak, more than 250,000 brain cells sprang into existence *each minute* within Helen's new brain.[25] That's more than four thousand new brain cells every single second!"

Ben paused to let the impression sink in.

"As this was going on, Helen's mother still felt no stirrings of new life. If she suspected there was a child within her, she could only imagine that it seemed to be very, very still. Yet can you sense how immensely *active* Helen's mortal blossoming actually was? Can you picture the intense, almost *chaotic* activity of those thousands of brain cells springing into existence second after second in every part of her brain?"

Ben paused again for emphasis, then continued. "Now, add to that picture another element. As Helen's brain cells formed, they sent out into that jumble of chaotic activity hundreds of tiny, threadlike extensions called axons and dendrites. These were the *connectors* that would link Helen's brain cells one to another. So, not only did thousands of brain cells spring up in Helen's brain every minute, millions of axons and dendrites also pushed forward, working their way into every corner of her brain, seeking to make the connections that would allow her to think. The marvel is that all those connections somehow got made *exactly right*. And that splendidly perfect jumble of chaotic activity brought Helen's power of mortal thought into existence!"

Kathy nodded in wide-eyed understanding.

"Now, one of your brain scientists, a man named Roger Sperry, who won the Nobel Prize in 1981, asked himself, in essence, how new brain cells know where to send their little connectors. How persistently, he wondered, do they seek to achieve their goal? So, using cells isolated from a tadpole's optic nerve, which is actually part of the brain, he put obstacles in the nerve track. The cells worked around the obstacles and made their proper connections. He made the obstacles more complex; the cells worked around them again. He forced the nerves into tortuous paths ever more distant from their original tracks, and the cells persistently made their connections. Finally, Sperry actually removed both eyes and put them in opposite sockets. The cells nonetheless recreated their original connections![26]

"Now, Kathy, Helen came into *physical* existence by the power represented there. You and I came into physical existence by the very same means. Can you see the incredible *intelligence* and *persistence* that a developing human brain represents?"

"I do, Ben. I do."

"And do you see, Kathy, that Helen just kept on doing the same thing after she was born—that she knew she had somewhere to go and simply overcame all obstacles until she got there."

"I *do* see that! It's marvelous!"

"You see, Kathy, Helen was simply expressing a natural property of her brain—one that we all share." Ben leaned forward, an impassioned look on his face. "*Intelligence and persistence exist inherently within us!*" he said, emphasizing each word. "Failing to *use* our intelligence and persistence violates the very meaning of who we are."

Ben settled into his chair again as Helen leaned forward to carry on.

"I want to share with you, Kathy, what happened

after my experience at the well. It wasn't part of the movie, so you may not know this. I returned to my bedroom. I had broken my doll in anger a short time before, smashing its head against the mantle of the fireplace. Now, as I entered the room, the memory of what I had done came back to me. I knelt down and desperately tried to find the pieces of my doll. I wanted to put her back together again, and when I couldn't, I wept. For the first time in my life, I felt remorse for something that I had done.[27] That is what *understanding* brought to me, Kathy. That is the *spiritual* consequence of the full and complete operation of all of those physical connections Ben just spoke about. And having experienced that remorse—which came, I know now, from sensing that I had violated my own nature as a daughter of God—I became able to see what I had done and to choose wiser paths thereafter. You see, Kathy, we're dealing with more than chemical reactions here."

Helen sat back in her chair, and Ben took over again. "Now, Kathy, Helen's persistence affected her brain in a very important way. On the day she was born she possessed virtually all of the brain cells she would ever possess. From that point on, however, some cells developed more fully and richly, while others withered and died. What do you suppose determined the difference?"

This was a principle Kathy readily understood. "The cells that developed were the ones that she used."

"Precisely! Nutrients and oxygen flowed into the cells that she used. The cells that she *didn't* use found themselves cut off from that sustaining flow, and they died. By her persisting, Helen gave form and shape to her brain. She *fashioned* her brain from raw potential as surely as Michelangelo fashioned the *David* from raw marble.[28]

"And this, you see, is why our *assignments* are so critical. They give direction, breadth, and shape to our capacities. They call upon us to *use* our faculties, to *extend* ourselves into areas we know nothing about. They call upon us to *exercise* our intelligence and persistence, and if we exercise our innate intelligence and persistence, we *enrich* ourselves. We call forth new axons and dendrites and form new and more complex interconnections within the networks of our brains. And we *see,* therefore, in ways that we otherwise might never have seen." He chuckled. "Forgive me. I'm speaking as if I were still mortal. The technical details are slightly different here, but the principle is the same."

Helen said, "You know, it occurs to me, Ben, that we might invite Joseph Campbell to join us."

"Excellent idea!" Ben said. "Do you know Joseph Campbell, Kathy?"

"He's the mythologist, isn't he? I saw a series about him on public television."

Ben nodded. "So you probably know the essentials of what he taught, but I agree with Helen that it would be wise to hear them again in this context, and directly from Joseph himself. Do you agree, Nicholas?"

"I was thinking the same thing myself," Nicholas said smiling.

"All right," Ben said. "I'll get another chair."

Joseph Campbell

By the time Ben returned to the group, Joseph Campbell was standing in their midst. Ben handled the introductions, and Joseph took his seat. Ben brought him up to date.

"We're sharing with Kathy Elliott—who is mortal, as you can see—the principles we operate by here. Will you please explain the ones you discovered, or should I say *re*discovered, through your work?"

"I'd be delighted, Ben." Joseph turned to Kathy. "You're Robby Barton's teacher, aren't you?" He smiled an insider's smile.

Kathy nodded, smiling back, somewhat surprised that he knew. "Yes, I am."

"Ben told me about his plan for Robby even before he presented it to the Council. I thought it was *wonderful!*" Joseph's eyes twinkled with delight.

"I'm recently arrived, Kathy. My graduation was little more than two earth years ago. I trust you understand what a pleasure it has been for me to associate constantly with people like these." He gestured to his three colleagues.

Kathy smiled. "I'm beginning to look forward to graduation myself."

This drew a laugh. "I understand!" Joseph said. "But don't forget to enjoy the homework while you're there!"

This drew a second laugh and a moment of shared amusement before they focused again on the task. Joseph assumed a more earnest demeanor, then began to explain.

"I studied myths, Kathy, which are far more than

simple stories. They express the deepest values of society. I had originally expected myths to vary greatly from culture to culture, suggesting that cultural values would differ as well. To a degree cultures do differ, of course, but not at the root of things. At the *root* of things, I discovered, they share a common myth."

Ben interrupted at this point. "Joseph, I forgot to mention. We're trying to give Kathy references she can use as she teaches. She won't be allowed to mention that she's met with us. Could you document your points from your earthly publications?"

"Of course, Ben." Turning to Kathy, he continued. "I describe this common myth in my book *The Hero with a Thousand Faces*. The essence of the myth is a journey. The journey begins with a 'call to adventure' in which the hero leaves the comfort he has known, and enters some 'zone unknown.' The zone unknown is a place of great danger, but also of great treasure. The hero may either accept the call to adventure or he may refuse it. If he accepts the call, he finds the treasure and is called home again, exalted. If he refuses the call, he loses both the treasure and his chance to return home.[29] Now, Kathy, do you see why I was so excited to hear of Ben's plan for Robby?"

Her eyes brightened with recognition. "Of course! It's the classical mythological journey."

"Yes. And it is particularly so because of the nature of the treasure Robby was seeking. You know what treasure Robby was seeking, don't you?"

Kathy reflected. "I would say it was understanding."

"That's right. And *that*, you see, is the essence of the myth. The treasure is never wealth, but understanding, or self-discovery. The hero, through the adventure, comes to know *himself*."

"Which is exactly what Robby did!"

"Precisely. Now, I believe you are also prepared to accept the other essential point of the common myth, particularly since you are here with us. I want to describe this essential point by quoting from my book. As I recite what I wrote, I want you to imagine it as it applies to Robby, whom you know so well. In fact, I'll use Robby's name to begin the quote." Joseph cleared his throat and began:

> [Robby's] perilous journey was a labor not of attainment but of reattainment, not discovery but *re*discovery.

Kathy closed her eyes, holding the image of Robby's adventure in her mind.

> The godly powers sought and dangerously won are revealed to have been within the heart of the hero all the time. He is *"the king's son"* who has come to know *who he is* and therewith has entered into the exercise of his proper power—*"God's son,"* who has learned to know how much that title means. From this point of view the hero is symbolical of that divine creative and redemptive image which is hidden within us all, only waiting to be known and rendered into life.[30]

Kathy opened her eyes. "Oh, my heavens!" she exclaimed.

Joseph chuckled. "Yes. Wisely put. You see, Kathy, the mythological journey is a metaphor for life itself.

And I have just come home."

Helen Keller said, "It is this very point—our experience of a common journey—that makes us equal. Many people admire what I did with my life because I seemed to be at such a disadvantage. But they're mistaken. If anything, I was greatly blessed. The *danger* in my 'zone unknown' was great, but so was the *treasure,* since eternal principles irrevocably link the two. And yet I see now that I was actually in no danger at all. The only *real* danger—and it would have been entirely *self*-imposed—was that I might turn from the adventure and refuse to accept the call."

"I *see,*" Kathy said thoughtfully.

Helen continued, seeking to anchor the point. "I want you to imagine two people, one of whom suddenly loses his sight, the other of whom, after a lifetime of blindness, suddenly *gains* his sight. Are their experiences different, or the same?"

"Well, one is a loss, the other a gain."

"Only on one level. At a higher level, both experiences, in Joseph's terms, are merely 'calls to adventure.' The newly sighted and the newly blind both find themselves in a 'zone unknown.' Their experiences differ in content, but not in principle, and that's truly all that we can say. Whether they gain or lose from their experiences depends entirely upon whether or not they accept the call to adventure—the *assignment* as we call it here."

Helen continued, "Even as a mortal I sensed the truth of this, and I expressed it in these words: 'We differ, blind and seeing, one from another, not in our senses, but in the use we make of them. The blind man of spirit faces the unknown and grapples with it, and what else does the world of seeing men do?'[31] Do you see, Kathy, how this principle transforms our apparent differences into a common quest?"

"I do. . . . But why does it seem so hard to accept?"

Helen paused for a moment, a contemplative expression on her face. "Well, let me put it this way. As a sixth-grade teacher, would you agree that you can quite easily divide your class into two groups—those who genuinely accept the assignments you give them and those who don't?"

"Yes. In general, I would agree."

"So, while the first group is busy doing their assignments, what is the other group doing?"

"Well, I'd say they're probably playing around, or moping, or complaining, or making excuses."

"The same two groups exist in mortal life itself, Kathy. Given your responsibility as the teacher of those young people, do you *accept* their complaints and excuses?"

"No. Of course not."

"Life doesn't either, and for the same reasons. Yet as uninspired mortals, before we've rediscovered who we really are, the only hope we seem able to grasp is the *mistaken* hope that if we complain and excuse ourselves long enough, life will somehow give in." Helen smiled at memories of herself doing that. "You know that I was also a complainer before I rediscovered myself and accepted *my* assignment, Kathy. And discovering that life doesn't respond to our complaints, even when we feel *most* justified, is often the first step toward wisdom."

Joseph Campbell took up the thread. "Do you know what the great danger of complaining is, Kathy?"

"I have some ideas," Kathy said, "but I'd rather hear yours."

"It's the simple fact that we can't complain and notice at the same time. It's both a physiological and spiritual impossibility. Complaining and noticing come from two absolutely different and completely incompatible mental and emotional states. So when we complain, we *instantly* cut off our ability to notice, which separates us from whatever we seek. Our greatest treasure could be right in front of our noses, and we wouldn't see it! That's the tragedy of complaining, which comes entirely from failing to see who we really are."

Joseph had been tugged forward in his chair, drawn there by the energy of his thoughts. Now, catching himself, he smiled, relaxed, and leaned back meditatively before going on.

"You know, I was always intrigued by the origin of the word *wisdom*. It is related to a Latin word that means 'to see.'[32] So wisdom and seeing are essentially the same thing. And I've always loved a verse in Proverbs that says this about wisdom: 'She is more precious than rubies: and all the things thou canst desire are not to be compared unto her.'[33] That, Kathy, is the cost of our complaining."

For a moment no one spoke. Finally, Ben leaned forward to retake the lead

"Now, Kathy," he said. "You must forgive us. We've become a bit intense. But only because we feel so deeply about these principles, and we see such a need for them in the people of your day. But I believe we ought to relax a moment, so why don't we take a break. We'll reconvene shortly. Would that be all right with you?"

Viktor Frankl

When the group reconvened, the circle had been enlarged by a sixth person, an elderly gentleman who sat next to Kathy and who, Kathy saw, was clearly mortal like herself. Ben explained.

"As you can see, Kathy, I've asked the assistance of another mortal. I needed someone with particular experiences and published works you can refer to. Our guest answered my need. I approached him last night, and he agreed to come. His name is Viktor Frankl."[34]

Kathy smiled delightedly. "Of course!"—she turned to Viktor—"You're the Austrian psychiatrist. I've read your book, *Man's Search for Meaning*. It's wonderful! I tell my students about you, but I'm afraid I didn't realize you were still mortal."

"I'm eighty-five years old," Viktor said graciously, "and I live in Vienna." He extended his hand, and Kathy shook it genially.

Ben smiled, heartened by their apparent good rapport. "As you know, Kathy, Viktor was a Jewish prisoner in the concentration camps during World War II. I've asked him to recount some of his experiences." Ben nodded to Viktor, and Viktor began.

"I was sitting one day in a most miserable mood—created, incidentally, by my own complaining—trying to figure out if I should trade my extra ration of sausage for a piece of bread. I became so exasperated with having to deal with such trivial concerns that I decided to pretend I was doing something else. So I imagined myself giving a lecture back in Vienna, and I picked as my topic the psychology of the concentration camp. As a consequence, I began reviewing my concentration-camp experiences from this more objective point of view."

Ben interrupted at this point. "What Viktor was doing, Kathy, was truly *noticing* for the first time. And I want *you* to notice how it affected him."

Viktor continued. "How it affected me was that it changed my perception of the camp completely. The misery I'd been experiencing softened. Its deep bitterness somehow went away. Things that had oppressed me now seemed bearable. My vision and my spirits cleared. Now, this was only my momentary experience of an imaginary lecture, but it occurred to me that I might apply the same principle in my day-to-day experiences. So from that moment on I became a noticer rather than a complainer, which blessed me immensely. You recall that story, don't you, Kathy? I wrote about it in my book."[35]

Kathy nodded assuringly. "I remember it well."

"Good. The point Ben asked me to emphasize is what I noticed. First of all, I noticed that I could easily discern two groups of prisoners: those who would survive and those who would not. And the difference, as you may recall from my book, was this: 'Most men in a concentration camp believed that the real opportunities of life had passed. Yet, in reality, there was an opportunity and a challenge. One could make a victory of those experiences, turning life into an inner triumph, or one could ignore the challenge and simply vegetate, as did a majority of the prisoners.' "[36]

Ben cut in, anxious that Kathy not miss the point. "Can you see, Kathy, that the concentration-camp experience amounted to a major assignment, and that the two groups of prisoners Viktor refers to were those who accepted the assignment and those who didn't?"

She hesitated, then said, "In a way I can, Ben, but your use of the word *assignment* in this context confuses me. To my mind, an assignment is something planned. Are you suggesting that God *arranged* the concentration camps or that He was somehow responsible for them, much as I am responsible for the homework I assign to my students?"

"Oh, heavens no!" Ben laughed, a bit chagrined at having unwittingly provoked such a misunderstanding. "God simply *allows* assignments of the sort Viktor experienced. He delegates also, of course, and we may consider our delegated duties to be assignments. And, in cases like Helen's where He has some deeply important mission that he knows a person will accept, He may take a gentle step or two, as I did with Robby, to place the person in a challenging circumstance. But the concentration camps and all other such ungodly and inhuman experiences are very different. They're created by the intersection of two eternal principles. First, when mortals fail to rediscover the vision of who they are, they become capable of doing horrible things to each other. Second, God cannot compel or coerce His children in even the tiniest degree. The very *principle* of Godhood, you see, is to possess wisdom sufficient to create, through love, a dominion that is *spontaneous* and not coerced. So, as His children fail to rediscover themselves, God cannot, by force, deny them the horrible things they wish to do. But He can, and does, *compensate* for those horrible things by designing within all of us the ability to transform such things into an equal measure of wisdom and strength. Our *assignment* in such cases—our only *burden,* if you wish—is to obey the principles involved. All other burdens are self-imposed. So in the end, you see, the only people harmed are those who persist in acting contrary to their true nature and those who refuse to obey the principles of growth—those who victimize and those who count themselves victims. Viktor is one of the few people in the camps who did neither. Does that help you understand?"

"Yes, thank you. It does."

"And by the way, the word *dominion* comes from a Latin root, *domus,* which means 'house,' or 'home.' The words *domestic* and *domicile* come from the same root.[37] So when I say that the essence of God-hood is to create, through love, a dominion that is spontaneous and not coerced, I mean that God's dominion is nothing more than the care a loving Father exercises for the family that He has created. And when He gives His mortal children dominion over the earth, He simply means, 'This is to be your home for a while. Care for it in wise and loving ways.'"

"How very interesting!"

Ben turned again to Viktor. "Now, Viktor, why don't you continue with the point you were making?"

Viktor nodded and went on. "I discovered, as I said, that the people who survived the concentration camps were those who found opportunities within them. Now, I would ask you, what sort of *opportunities* do you suppose existed within the concentration camps?"

Kathy considered the question, recalling her

memories of Viktor's book, but found those particular memories elusive. "I don't know," she said.

Viktor said, "Let me quote you what I said in *Man's Search for Meaning*. 'We who lived in the concentration camps can remember the men who walked through the huts comforting others, giving away their last piece of bread. They may have been few in number, but they offer sufficient proof that everything can be taken from a man but one thing: the last of the human freedoms—to choose one's attitude in any given set of circumstances, to choose one's own way.' "[38]

As Viktor recalled his experiences, his eyes showed a glistening of tears. *He is touched,* Kathy thought, *not by the suffering, but by the goodness.*

"You see, Kathy, the opportunity existed for us to support one another. Those who died did so mostly of loneliness, for they were, by *their* choice, separated from those of us who remembered our power to love."

Ben cut in gently again. "And they were separated, more tragically, from their Father. You asked, Kathy, if God arranged the concentration camps. No, He didn't. But was He present within them? Yes, He was—in the thoughts and actions of prisoners like Viktor who, within those camps, came to understand that they are His children. God's love, you see, is simply an abstraction to mortals until they, by *their* loving, make it real. Viktor was blessed to love, Kathy, and so he was blessed to survive."

A moment passed in thoughtful silence. Then Viktor spoke again.

"Now, Kathy. I must make something clear. I've been speaking of *spiritual* death and *spiritual* life.

Among those who died *physically* were those whose spirits soared. And among those who *survived* physically were those whose spirits had become degraded and deformed. The issue in the camps, you see, was to survive *spiritually,* and that is what most prisoners failed to see."

Ben stepped in again to amplify the thought. "Surviving spiritually is *always* the issue, Kathy. To die *physically* is nothing—simply a matter of moving on. The issue is whether the moving on carries us home, as Joseph so elegantly explained a few moments ago, or into an exile that is ultimately more tragic than the concentration camps themselves. To survive spiritually, we must love one another. This is the point Robby understood when he saw that a red petticoat couldn't become Old Glory on its own. Mortals must work together and help each other grow. When they fail to do that, they jeopardize their spiritual survival, no less so today than in the concentration camps of World War II. In either case, our fate, you will learn, is to receive the companionship of people as loving or unloving as ourselves.[39] 'Do unto others,' Kathy, 'as you would have others do unto you,' for that is the principle by which justice is accomplished."

Ben turned to Viktor. "Thank you, Viktor, for having come, and for having lived worthy of the wisdom you've shared with us today."

Ben stood. Viktor and Nicholas followed. Turning to Kathy, Viktor said, "I'm honored," then, leaning toward her, he kissed her on the cheek. He kissed Helen in the same fashion, then shook hands with Nicholas, and with Ben, who embraced him. Then he turned and walked out of the circle and out of sight.

Ben and Nicholas took their seats, and Ben took up where he'd left off. "We're talking about *responsibility,* Kathy—about facing bravely and lovingly the challenges life places before us. As Viktor wrote in his book, 'Life ultimately means taking the responsibility to find the right answer to its problems and to fulfill the tasks which it constantly sets for each individual.'[40] America faces danger, Kathy, because too few people are willing to do that—to be *personally* responsible for the challenges they face. One problem this creates is that people turn too often to government for answers, and government, which has no *personal* answers,[41] is too often willing to oblige."

Isaac Newton

"You may find it strange, Kathy, that I've invited Isaac Newton to discuss the political side of our issue, but his presence is more relevant than it might first appear. Would you like to explain the relevance, Isaac?"

"Thank you, Ben. First of all, Kathy, when I discovered the beautifully simple principle of gravitational attraction, I felt humbled that God had blessed me to see it. And when I came to understand the mathematical principles behind the orderly movements of the heavens, I gratefully accepted those principles as His laws and as evidence of His existence. In my book *Mathematical Principles of Natural Philosophy* I explained my feelings in these words: 'This most beautiful system of the sun, planets, and comets, could only proceed from the counsel and dominion of an intelligent and powerful Being. This Being governs all things. And from his true dominion it follows that the true God is a living, intelligent, and powerful Being, [who] knows all things that are or can be done.'[42] Obviously, I have since confirmed those observations. Do you follow me so far?"

Kathy nodded.

"Good. I hope I can keep it simple."

He smiled, and Kathy felt warmed by his concern.

"I wanted to establish my own beliefs in the beginning to point out that they correspond exactly with those that existed at the founding of your great nation. The authors of your founding documents"—Isaac turned to Ben and smiled—"including this gentleman who sits here to my right—took great care to explain exactly where they stood. In your Declaration of Independence, for example, they declared that they held it *self-evident* that all human beings are created equal, and that they are endowed by their Creator with certain unalienable rights. A 1793 United States Supreme Court decision also declares that 'MAN, fearfully and wonderfully made, is the workmanship of his all perfect CREATOR.'[43] Now, Kathy, do you see how clearly your founding fathers declared what they held 'self-evident' about the nature of the citizens of their new nation?"

Kathy nodded that she did.

"Within their set of self-evident truths, they included another assumption, directly related to the first, about the source of the wisdom that would guide the new nation. I can best illustrate *this* assumption by quoting from two other Supreme Court decisions, one rendered in 1823, the other in 1840. The first decision refers to 'those principles of abstract justice, which the Creator of all things has impressed on the mind of his creature man.'[44] The second declares that, in the absence of clear precedent, legal judgments shall be based on 'the source of eternal justice as it comes from intelligence and truth.'[45] As someone who has personally experienced the spiritual discernment of truth, Kathy, is there any question in your mind as to what those early jurists were referring to?"

"No," she said. "There isn't."

"Good. Now, as the nineteenth century progressed, those early assumptions began to weaken, and another assumption—a very different assumption—began to take their place. By 1887, this new assumption had been clearly expressed in a Supreme

Court decision as follows: 'Out of the domain of the exact sciences and actual observation there is no absolute certainty.'[46] Do you see the shift?"

Kathy nodded. "Yes, I do. Ben and the other founding fathers assumed that we have an inherent *spiritual* capacity for discerning the truth; the new assumption attempts to establish science as the only certain source of truth. These are obviously very different assumptions leading to very different conclusions."

"That's correct. Now, I want you to see something very clearly. Your laws declare unquestionably that the *provisions* of the Constitution may not be changed without due process. Yet, I would argue, Kathy, that *underlying assumptions* are as important as specific provisions, and yet here, as you can see, *without due process,* the assumptions underlying your Constitution have been changed!"[47]

With those words Kathy began to sense the enormity of what she was hearing. She sat more erect, and leaned forward, eager to let nothing slip by. Isaac continued to explain.

"Ben invited me here because, indirectly, I am responsible for that shift, and I would like to have a hand in correcting it. The problem, you see, was my success. With nothing more than my calculus, the law of gravity, and my basic laws of motion, I was able to calculate in two hours courses of planetary movement that my predecessors, Johannes Kepler and Tycho Brahe, had spent sixty years discovering through observation alone. I even corrected their errors.[48] This astounded me, and it astounded the scientists of my time. Even today, your scientists use my methods to exactly calculate eclipses of the moon and sun hundreds of years into the future or the past, or even to successfully land an unmanned shuttle on a tiny section of earth, as the Russians have recently done."

Isaac continued, "The first consequence of my success was to inspire within me a profound sense of humility and thankfulness. Unfortunately, humility in the face of success is difficult to maintain, and my success also inspired a number of unfortunate consequences. For example, the great poet Alexander Pope suggested this for my epitaph: 'Nature and Nature's laws lay hid in night: / God said, let Newton be! and all was light.' "[49]

Isaac laughed gently and shook his head, embarrassed.

"I cite that only to point out the arrogance such success can inspire. In fact, we began to believe that through scientific principles we could achieve the same degree of success in any area of life. We began to see ourselves doing God's work, using our scientific knowledge to overcome poverty, war, disease, ignorance, and every other ill known to mankind. We called our belief 'determinism,' because we believed that everything was determined by the precise operation of natural law. In seeking to cure the world's ills through science, our motives were of the noblest sort, but we suffered from a common failing—one that Ben so often points out. We believed that we were seeing all that there was to see, when the fact is, mortals never do. Not realizing that fact, however, we began to ignore the need for faith.

"Now, let me point out a few of the things we

didn't see. First of all, we didn't see that something existed other than the *forces of attraction*. By 'forces of attraction,' I mean things like gravity, which was my specialty, and the electromagnetic attractions that hold molecules together. We assumed that wholes were formed and held together by these *attractions* and that science was simply a matter of discovering the attractive forces and quantifying them mathematically. You see the principle don't you, Kathy? Am I being too vague?"

"I believe I understand, Isaac. I suppose it's like a child with a kite." She laughed. "You can tell I teach sixth grade. The kite and the child are connected by the string, and you assumed everything in nature was held together by the same principle—parts connected to parts, with these 'attractive forces' acting the role of the string."

"Yes," Isaac said beaming. "A very apt analogy. Your students are very fortunate. Now, to show you how important this idea of *attractive forces* was to us, let me cite another poem written about me by the son of the great French scientist Ampere: 'Announcing the coming of Science's Messiah / . . . He came, he revealed the principle supreme, / Eternal, universal, One and unique as God himself. / The worlds were hushed, he spoke: ATTRACTION. / This word was the very word of creation.' "[50]

Isaac cleared his throat and shook his head, his discomfort showing in his face.

"Kathy, I hope you understand that I'm not citing these statements for what they say about me. I'm simply trying to show you the spirit of the times I lived in and the high aspirations we had for our new scientific powers. You see, that same spirit existed—those same high aspirations existed—when those Supreme Court justices, 160 years after my death, declared science the only certain source of truth."

She smiled reassuringly. "I understand completely, Isaac. I'm finding this fascinating. Please go on."

"Now, I will show you how we were mistaken. I will show you what it was that we didn't see. It's so simple, I'm almost embarrassed to talk about it. But things are never simple when you don't see them, are they? Now, I want you to imagine *ice*. Ice is solid because of the strong *attractive forces* involved. Do you see that, Kathy?"

"Yes, I do."

"Now imagine that we heat the ice. We are allowing the energy of heat to flow into it. Do you see that as well?"

"Yes."

"Good. Now, as the temperature reaches thirty-two degrees Fahrenheit, what happens?"

"The ice turns to water."

"As you can see, the attractive forces, *though they are as strong as they ever were,* no longer predominate. What exists now is a combination—a *balance,* if you will—between the attractive forces on the one hand, and the flowing energy of heat on the other."

"I see that."

"Good. So we allow still more heat energy to flow through the water. Its temperature rises again, and, as it reaches 212 degrees Fahrenheit, *now* what happens?"

"The water turns to steam."

"Correct. And what is the relationship *now* between the attractive forces and the flowing energy of heat. Are they still balanced?"

"No. The flowing energy of heat predominates. The attractive forces hardly operate at all."

"Exactly. The flowing energy of heat has essentially broken the attractive bonds, overwhelmed the attractive forces, *which have not themselves changed throughout the entire process!*[51]

"And this shows you what we didn't see. We built all of our propositions around the attractive forces *alone,* and they are, at best, *half* the picture—and not even the half that produces the differences! Do you see that?"

"I *do!*"

"Good. Now let me tell you something else that we didn't see. A very important state exists in nature that we call 'equilibrium.' Equilibrium, essentially, is stillness. Few things in nature exist at absolute equilibrium, because few things are absolutely still. As a consequence, natural systems generally don't exist *at* equilibrium, but various distances *away* from equilibrium, or away from stillness, lifted there by flowing energy, which may be weak, as in the case of ice, or strong, as in the case of steam. Now, based on this principle, which of the two—ice or steam—is *closest* to equilibrium? Which is most *still?*"

"Ice, obviously."

"Yes. Now, let me ask you this question: which is easiest to predict: the behavior of ice or the behavior of steam?"

"Obvious again: the behavior of ice."

"That's correct. Ice is easier to predict than steam

because of this simple principle: *the closer a system is to equilibrium, the more predictable it is*. As systems move *away* from equilibrium, or away from stillness, they get harder to predict. And Kathy, if they move away from equilibrium *far* enough, they become *impossible* to predict.[52] Can you see how that would be the case?"

"Yes."

"Now, I want you to see how these principles explain my apparent success. You know that I studied our solar system. Relative to all of the others aspects of nature that I might have chosen to study, would you say that our solar system is *close* to equilibrium, or *far* from equilibrium?"

"Well, relative to all other aspects of nature, I'd say that our solar system is quite *close* to equilibrium."

"And what would you say, therefore, about how easy it should be, relatively speaking, to predict the behavior of the particular aspect of nature that I chose to study? Would you expect it to be easy or hard?"

"Well, once you figured out the method, I'd say it would be *easy* to predict. After all, it's close to equilibrium, and look at the results you achieved."

"Yes. I was quite fortunate, wasn't I? I just happened to pick a system that is so close to equilibrium that it is almost entirely predictable. I discovered the constant attractive force of gravity, and in a system so close to equilibrium, that is all that mattered. As a consequence, for my little discovery I was hailed as 'Science's Messiah,' and we genuinely believed, based on that tiny achievement, that we had found *in science* the secret key to the mind of God. Again, this was also the state of mind of those Supreme Court justices who overruled what Ben and his colleagues originally assumed by exalting science as the source of truth.

"I'm inclined to ask again, Kathy, if you are still understanding me, but I don't wish to underestimate you, nor do I wish to unduly burden you. I think you are doing remarkably well so far."

"Thank you, Isaac. I'm finding your ideas very stimulating."

He smiled affectionately. "That pleases me. Now, you can see the mistake we made. We assumed that my simple methods would apply to *all* aspects of nature, even to those aspects that exist far from equilibrium, like the human body, the societies we lived in, or even the fundamental properties of life itself. But we ran into problems almost immediately.

"For example, I tried to study the simple pendulum. But my methods wouldn't work, even for a simple pendulum. The reason was friction. You see, friction represents one of those sources of flowing energy. The energy of friction leaves the system and is gone. That tiny fact was enough to render my calculations wrong! So we began to pretend that friction didn't matter, that we could somehow *ignore* it. We invented the *ideal pendulum!* This is a pendulum without friction. No such thing exists, of course, but we had to *assume* that it existed, as some sort of underlying principle, or as an underlying ideal form. This let us *simplify* nature—rid ourselves of anything confusing. Otherwise our methods wouldn't work. This idea blossomed into the *experimental method,* whose purpose is to isolate things, to get rid of confusing factors, including those that belong to that *other* aspect of nature, the dimension of flowing energy, the one we were choosing to ignore because it ruined our ability to predict.[53] If you wish, Kathy, you may observe this principle at work in the double-blind research design that so much of medical science is based on. Its purpose is to rid medicine of the annoying presence of the flowing energies of the human mind. Yet how often do the things claimed to have been proved by such simplified experiments turn out later to be *dis*proved by the complex reality of experience?[54]

"I point this out, Kathy, because the simple science that I invented, which properly applies only to systems that exist close to equilibrium, has been transformed by some into a tool for governing. As a consequence, if you decide to govern your life by some principle that fits *your* intuitive sense of truth but doesn't match the orthodox scientific view, government authorities may deny you freedom to apply your principle unless you prove it to *their* satisfaction by the methods of experimental science. Or if those authorities wish to impose something on you that you feel is wrong, they will often claim to have proved it correct—and you wrong—by those very same methods.[55] Yet the experimental methods of deterministic science do *not* apply to systems as far from equilibrium as the bodies you mortals occupy nor the societies you live in.[56] If Karl Marx were here, he could tell you that what I'm saying is true. Communism was his plan for applying deterministic science to governing, and look what's come of it now.

"This linking of science and government is not accidental. It flows directly from our deterministic point of view.[57] We honestly believed that our scientific methods, coupled with our honorable intentions, gave us the right and the ability to determine what was best for other people. Even in your day, Kathy, a UNESCO document points out that there are those who 'consider that the recent triumph of science entitles it at last to rule over the whole of culture.'[58] What is at fault here is not science, but our wish to *limit* science to a single dimension and to use it as a tool to deny the value of *other* methods of discerning the truth."

"Now, Kathy, forgive my burdening you with such a long discourse, but I see that you are following me quite well. I would like to point out just one more thing. Are you up to it?"

"I am, Isaac. But I want to mention something. I know very little about science—only what I teach to my sixth graders—but it seems to me that much of what you are saying is common sense. I appreciate your taking time to explain it to me, and I've not found it boring at all. Quite the contrary, in fact. But I'm afraid I'll have a hard time explaining it to anyone else. And Ben has been suggesting that you all give me some earthly references that I can refer to. What would you suggest I read?"

"Obviously, none of my own works refer to these principles. In general, most people respond well to commonsense examples of the sort I've tried to give you. But if you wish to study the science involved, I would direct you to the area known as 'chaos theory,' or 'nonlinear thermodynamics.' A number of nontechnical references exist."[59]

"Thank you. Now, please proceed."

"All right. In conclusion, I want to show you what is probably the most important difference between close-to-equilibrium systems, like our solar system, and far-from-equilibrium systems, like the mortal human body and the societies mortal humans live in. This difference is also one of the things that my colleagues and I failed to see.

"Imagine water flowing very strongly in your bathroom sink, in through the faucet and out through the drain. The water obviously strikes the sink and swirls around before flowing out again. If you examine the swirling carefully, you will see that it forms a pattern and that the pattern persists. If you place your hand within the pattern, you disturb it. But if you then *remove* your hand, the pattern returns. Can you picture that?"

"Yes, I can."

"My point is that the pattern of the flowing is *self-regulating*. Not only does it sustain itself, if you disturb it, it also *restores* itself. One of the greatest discoveries of recent science is that this property of *self-regulation* emerges spontaneously in systems that exist far from equilibrium.[60] Close to equilibrium, where little energy flows, this capacity to sustain a dynamic, self-regulating pattern weakens and eventually dies. Can you see that this is true?"

"Yes."

"I've spoken very simply here, Kathy, using the simplest examples of the simplest kinds of energy. Yet the principles apply throughout all levels of nature,[61] including the human mind and spirit. In dynamic systems that exist far from equilibrium, *self-regulation exists!* This is the single fact that my colleagues and I, from our narrow perspective, could not possibly have imagined, and therefore refused to accept. All we could see was that nature consisted of some ultimate tiny particles connected by some ultimate attractive forces, and these became the objects of our searching. We eventually came to see no source of order, no source of truth, and no source of power but our own.

"And it frightened us. We witnessed the existence of so many degrading human qualities and conditions, and we concluded that there was no hope for humankind unless order could somehow be *imposed*. And who better to do the imposing than those of us who possessed the unerring 'fountain of truth'? These thoughts are not inherent in science itself, but they have become the credo of some who, often with the noblest of intentions, now wish to turn science into a political tool. This has been, to me, a source of great sadness.

"You see, in seeking to impose *our* order, we sincerely believed, in the beginning at least, that we were God's agents, doing His work, not realizing that we were simply presuming to take His place. We had exalted the power of the mind, yet the mind, I see now, is but an instrument of the heart, and the heart is an instrument of God. In our arrogance we began to violate the first principle of His Godhood, which is that dominion must be spontaneous and not coerced. The existence of *self*-regulation means that order *cannot* be imposed from the outside, not long-term, at least, and any government, or any other human enterprise, that ignores this principle is doomed in the end to fail. You have in your possession a small chunk of gray concrete that proves it."

Isaac stopped speaking, his thoughts concluded. For a moment no one spoke, then Ben picked up the theme.

"When we wrote the Constitution, Kathy, we were discussing these very principles, though we could not have conceived them in these terms. We only knew that we had won from the British the right to govern, and the Constitution was to be our instrument for delegating that right—certain portions of it to the nation and others to the states.

"But we also saw that those delegated rights of government rest upon a much more fundamental right—upon an ultimate *power* of government that descends from our relationship with God. The Constitution also became our instrument for protecting that power—for guaranteeing in law what was already true in fact: that this ultimate power of government— the one upon which all others depend—must forever remain exactly where God placed it—in the hearts and minds of His children. Otherwise, we believed, our new nation could not endure.[62]

"*You* have that ultimate power, Kathy, and the responsibility to sustain it. So do your sixth-grade students, and your friends and neighbors, and all of the other ordinary citizens of the nation that in some small measure I helped to create. Nicholas gave his *life* for the right to exercise that power. The patriots of Fort Stanwix gave all *they* had for it, and so did all of the others who participated in that great national assignment. We faced our 'zone unknown,' Kathy, and our power to govern—our true power as children of God—was the treasure we found.

"Now the treasure is yours. But to keep it, you

must understand it and you must accept it, so let me make an important distinction. As a teacher, you have certain *delegated* rights. These delegated rights give you limited and temporary powers that you may use wisely and lovingly to govern your sixth-grade students. Government officials have similar delegated rights, which are temporary and limited as yours are, and carry with them the same obligation that they be used in wise and loving ways. The *ultimate* power of mortal government is much more fundamental, and it rests with each of you individually. *Your* ultimate power, Kathy, which God gave to you and only your own failure to honor principle can take away, is the power and the responsibility to govern *whom?*"

Kathy felt upon her the caring eyes of five wonderful friends. "Myself," she said.

"Yes. That is the key. This has always been a principle of God. Isaac has shown you that it is also a principle of science. In this instance, you see, science has revealed a principle of God."

The Assignment

"We've concluded, Kathy. The time has come that you must go. As you know, we invited you here on the condition that you accept a very important assignment. You have indicated your willingness to do so. I will explain that assignment now.

"You have rediscovered your true nature. You now know exactly who you are. Your assignment, Kathy, is this: be true to yourself. *Honor your nature as a child of God.* In the end, that is the only assignment that there has ever been."

Ben stood. The others followed. They embraced Kathy in turn, Ben last of all. As they separated, Kathy smiled and said, "When I get back, Ben, I'm going to buy me a red petticoat."

Ben reached behind himself, then turned to Kathy and said, "Please. Take this one. This is the original 'red petticoat'—the first Old Glory that flew over Fort Stanwix. We'd like you to hang it in place of the one Ben Harding helped you make. It's invaluable, of course. But don't worry. It will be protected. No one but you and Robby will ever know what it is. We simply believe it would be helpful to have it present again where mortals may be exposed to it. That will be mainly you and your students, but from small things, great things will grow. Will you accept it?"

Kathy hesitated for a moment, then she extended her hands, and Ben placed Old Glory in them. "Oh, thank you Ben!" she said.

"Will you honor it?" he asked.

"I will," she said.

And in an instant, she was gone.

PART 3

Notes

1. *Fort Stanwix.* "Fort Stanwix (known in this campaign to the patriots as Fort Schuyler,) was built in 1758 against the French. The next year, the French met with those disasters which in 1760, gave Canada to the English, and thereafter Fort Stanwix served only for purposes of Indian trade, and as a protection to the carry between the Mohawk and Wood Creek. It had been a favorite place for peaceful meeting with the Indians. Naturally it had lost its military strength, and when in April, 1777, Colonel Gansevoort occupied it with the third regiment of the New York line, it was sadly out of repair. The plans for its reconstruction were yet in progress when St. Leger appeared before it. But care and labor had been so effectual that the broken walls had been restored, and the ruins which the invader came to overrun had given place to defenses too strong for his attack." Ellis H. Roberts, *The Battle of Oriskany: Its Place in History* (Utica, NY: Ellis H. Roberts, 1877), 8.

2. *Colonel Peter Gansevoort.* "Col. Peter Gansevoort, who was in command, was a native of Albany, now twenty-eight years of age. He had been with Montgomery before Quebec, and there won his rank as colonel. His conduct here was admirable. The courage of youth did not prevent on his part a wisdom worthy of much riper years." Ibid. "Peter Gansevoort . . . lies buried in the Albany Rural Cemetery. The inscription on the modest monument of white marble . . . reads: TO THE MEMORY OF PETER GANSEVOORT, JUN. A BRIGADIER GENERAL IN THE ARMY OF THE UNITED STATES, WHO

DIED ON THE 2nd DAY OF JULY 1812, AGED 62 YEARS 11 MONTHS & 16 DAYS. . . . HERE STANWIX CHIEF AND BRAVE DEFENDER LIES." John Albert Scott, "Appendix to Volume I of Fort Stanwix and Oriskany," in John Albert Scott, *Fort Stanwix (Fort Schuyler) and Oriskany* (Rome, NY: Rome Sentinel Company, 1927), 7. This appendix is a separate and undated seven-page insert apparently placed unattached in the book.

3. *Lieutenant Colonel Marinus Willet.* "With [Gansevoort] as Lieutenant Colonel was Marinus Willett, a native of New York city, aged thirty-seven, trained in the French war and the invasion of Canada, a dashing soldier, ready for any adventure, and shrewd in all the ways of border war." Roberts, 8–9.

4. *Lieutenant Colonel Mellon.* "The garrison consisted of seven hundred and fifty men. It was composed of Gansevoort's own regiment, the Third New York, with two hundred men under Lieutenant Colonel Mellon of Colonel Wesson's regiment of the Massachusetts line. Colonel Mellon had fortunately arrived with a convoy of boats filled with supplies, on the second of August, when the enemy's fires were already in sight only a mile away. This was the force with which Gansevoort was to hold the fort." Ibid., 9.

5. *"People call it 'Old Glory.'"* Calling the Fort Stanwix flag "Old Glory" is actually an anachronism. The original "Old Glory" was "so named by Captain William Driver of Salem, Massachusetts, in 1824 when his mother and female friends presented him with the results of their

handiwork in the form of the flag." The original "Old Glory" has twenty-four stars and is preserved in the Smithsonian Institution. William Rea Furlong and Byron McCandless, *So Proudly We Hail: The History of the United States Flag* (Washington, DC: Smithsonian Institution Press, 1981), 190.

Some historians also suggest that the flag raised at Fort Stanwix was not the "stars and stripes," but the "Continental flag," which had the thirteen stripes, but carried the British cross rather than stars on the blue field. "There would appear to be two main contentions offered in favor of the cross. One is the use of the term 'Continental flag' by both Colbrath and Willett, and the other is the carving upon a powder horn reputed to have been cut by a soldier in garrison at Fort Stanwix. As for the term 'Continental,' the observant reader will have noted it employed in various letters quoted in preceding chapters just as 'national' is used today. There were regimental flags and continental flags, but no national flags at that period. It may be safely assumed that whether the red, white and blue ensign had a cross or a constellation of stars, it would have been 'the Continental flag' to contemporary writers." Scott, 349–50. See also Furlong and McCandless, 102–5.

6. *Abraham Swartout's coat.* Abraham Swartout apparently volunteered his blue coat less enthusiastically than the story portrays. Colonel Gansevoort's papers include this letter (cited in Scott, 351) that he received from Abraham Swar-

tout about a year after the battle:

"Dear Sir: The great distance which Your duty calls us Appart obliges me at this time to give You this trouble which Otherwise I would not. You may Remember agreeable to Your promise, I was to have an Order for Eight Yards of Broad-Cloth, on the Commissary for Cloathing of this State, in lieu of my Blue Cloak, which was used for Coulours at Fort Schuyler [Fort Stanwix]—an Opportunity now presenting itself—I beg You to send me an Order, inclosed to Mr. Jeremiah Rensseler, pay Master at Albany or to Mr. Henry Van Veghtem, Albany, where I will receive it, and You will oblige me—who will Always acknowledge the same with true gratitude—

Please to make my Compts. to the Other Officers of the Regiment. I am, Dear Sir Your Hble Serv't

Abraham Swartout, Capt."

7. *Molly Winder's red petticoat.* "There have been several names advanced in connection with the honor of having supplied the red and the white materials, but none so well substantiated; the red has been commonly accepted as having come from a woman's flannel petticoat, while Colonel Willett says 'ammunition shirts' were used for the white stripes." Ibid., 176.

8. *"General" Barry St. Leger.* "Lieutenant Colonel Barry St. Leger had been chosen by the king himself, on Burgoyne's nomination. . . . In the regular army of England he became an ensign in

1756, and coming to America the next year he had served in the French war, and learned the habits of the Indians, and of border warfare. In some local sense, perhaps as commanding this corps, he was styled a brigadier. His regular rank was Lieutenant Colonel of the thirty-fourth regiment." Ibid., 10.

9. *Joseph Brant.* "Inferior to St. Leger in rank, but superior to him in natural powers and in personal magnetism, was Joseph Brant—Thayendanegea—chief of the Mohawks. He had been active in arraying the Six Nations on the side of King George, and only the Oneidas and Tuscaroras had refused to follow his lead. He was now thirty-five years of age; in figure the ideal Indian, tall and spare and lithe and quick; with all the genius of his tribe, and the training gained in Connecticut schools, and in the family of Sir William Johnson." Ibid.

10. *John Johnson.* "Sir John Johnson led the regiments which had been organized from the settlers in the Mohawk valley. He had inherited from his father, Sir William, the largest estate held on the continent by any individual, William Penn excepted. He had early taken sides with the King against the colonists, and having entered into a compact with the patriots to preserve peace and remain at Johnstown, he had violated his promise, and fled to Canada. He came now with a sense of personal wrong, to recover his possessions and to resume the almost royal sway which he had exercised." Ibid., 11.

11. *Nicholas Herkimer.* (As you'll see in the following

quotes, historians don't always agree about how to spell Nicholas Herkimer's last name.) "Colonel Gansevoort had appealed to the Committee of Safety for Tryon county, for help. Its chairman was Nicholas Herchkeimer, (known to us as Herkimer,) who had been appointed a brigadier general by Congress in the preceding autumn. . . . He was now forty-eight years of age, short, slender, of dark complexion, with black hair and bright eyes." Ibid., 15.

12. *The ambush.* "Harkheimer had to cross a deep, crooked ravine, with a marshy bottom and its rivulet, drained, traversed and spanned by a causeway and bridge of logs. Sir John [Johnson]completely enveloped this spot with marksmen, leaving an inlet for the Americans to enter and no outlet by which to escape. Moreover he placed his best troops—whites—on the road westward, to bar all access to the fort. . . .

"Harkheimer's column, without scouts or flankers, plunged into the ravine and had partially climbed the opposite crest and attained the plateau, when, with his wagon train huddled together in the bottom, the environing forest and dense underwood was alive with enemies and alight with the blaze of muskets and rifles, succeeded by yells and war whoops, just as the shattering lightning is almost simultaneous with the terrifying thunder." J. Watts de Peyster, "Oriskany," *Magazine of American History* (January 1878), 24.

13. *The rainstorm.* "Then a slaughter ensued, such as never has occurred upon this continent, and if the

Americans had not displayed heroic bravery they would have been exterminated at once. Most likely they would have been so eventually, had not Heaven interposed at the crisis and let down a deluge of rain, which stopped the slaughter, since in the day of flint locks firing amid torrents of rain was an impossibility." Ibid., 24–25.

14. *On Nicholas Herkimer's brother being one of St. Leger's captains.* "Harkheimer's brother was not only a sort of Quartermaster to St. Leger, but especially charged with the supervision of the Indian auxiliaries, who were the cause of the General's death and the slaughter of so many of their common kinsmen, connections, friends and neighbors." Ibid., 26.

15. *Herkimer's wound.* "Almost at the first volley, Harkheimer was desperately wounded in the leg by a shot, which likewise killed his horse. He caused his saddle to be placed at the foot of a beech tree, and there sitting upon it and propped against the trunk, he lit his pipe, and while quietly smoking continued to give orders and make dispositions which saved all that escaped." Ibid., 25.

16. *On White Fawn fighting with Nicholas Herkimer.* The idea of including White Fawn in the story came from this reference: "Tradition relates that an Oneida maid, only fifteen years old, daughter of a chief, fought on the side of the patriots, firing her rifle, and shouting her battle cry." The source given for this reference is a "newspaper report of a tradition in the family of George Wagner, a survivor." Roberts, 22.

17. *On Herkimer's death.* "He behaved like a perfect

hero and perished a martyr to Liberty, for he died in his own home at Danube, two miles below Little Falls, ten days afterwards (16th August), of a bungling amputation and subsequent ignorant treatment." de Peyster, 25.

18. *On the idea that Nicholas Herkimer's stand at Oriskany turned the war around.* "The turning point of the Burgoyne Campaign and of the American Revolution was the battle of Oriskany on the 6th of August, 1777. . . .

"Harkheimer's little army suffered a disastrous *tactical* defeat. That this did not remain a defeat, and was transmuted into an eventual success, was due to the common-sense generalship of Harkheimer. . . .

"It was Harkheimer who knocked all the fight out of the Indians, and it was the desertion of the Indians that rendered St. Leger's expedition abortive. . . .

"The gist of all this . . . concentrates in one fact:—it was not the defense of Fort Stanwix but the heroism of Harkheimer's militia that saved the Mohawk Valley, and constitutes Oriskany . . . the crisis and turning point against the British of the Burgoyne campaign, and the 'Decisive Conflict' of America's seven years war for Independence." Ibid., 22, 26, 28, 29.

19. *Benjamin Franklin's "If life were a book" idea.* "When I reflect, as I frequently do, upon the felicity I have enjoyed, I sometimes say to myself, that, were the offer made me, I would engage to run again, from beginning to end, the same career of life. All I would ask, should be the privilege of

an author, to correct in a second edition, certain errors of the first." Tryon Edwards, comp., *The New Dictionary of Thoughts: A Cyclopedia of Quotations*, rev. and enl. ed. (N.p.: Standard Book Company, 1966), 360. When Franklin was a young man, he wrote the following epitaph for himself: "The body of / B. Franklin, printer / (Like the cover of an old book, / Its contents torn out / And stripped of its lettering and gilding), / Lies here, food for worms. / But the work shall not be lost; / For it will (as he believed) appear once more / In a new and more elegant edition, / Revised and corrected / By the Author." Andrew M. Allison, *The Real Benjamin Franklin* (Salt Lake City, UT: Freemen Institute, 1982), 276.

20. *"The longer I live, the more convincing proofs I see . . ."* Benjamin Franklin, *The Writings of Benjamin Franklin*, ed. Albert Henry Smyth, 10 vols. (New York: Macmillan Company, 1905–7), 9:600–601.

21. *"A breath of will blows . . ."* Ralph Waldo Emerson, *The Conduct of Life, Nature, and Other Essays* (London: J. M. Dent, n.d.), 164.

22. On March 30, 1863, President Abraham Lincoln declared a National Fast Day. His proclamation included these words: "We have been the recipients of the choicest bounties of Heaven. We have been preserved, these many years, in peace and prosperity. We have grown in numbers, wealth and power, as no other nation has ever grown. But we have forgotten God. We have forgotten the gracious hand which preserved us in peace, and multiplied and enriched and

strengthened us; and we have vainly imagined, in the deceitfulness of our hearts, that all these blessings were produced by some superior wisdom and virtue of our own. Intoxicated with unbroken success, we have become too self-sufficient to feel the necessity of redeeming and preserving grace, too proud to pray to the God that made us!" Abraham Lincoln, *The Collected Works of Abraham Lincoln*, ed. Roy P. Basler, 8 vols. (New Brunswick, NJ: Rutgers University Press, 1953), 6:156.

23. *Marcus Aurelius quote.* Marcus Aurelius, "The Meditations of Marcus Aurelius Antoninus," trans. George Long, in *Harvard Classics*, ed. Charles Eliot (Danbury, CT: Grolier Enterprises, 1980), 200, italics added.

24. *"Faith is a mockery . . ."* Helen Keller, *The World I Live in* (New York: Century, 1910), 92–94, italics added.

25. *250,000 brain cells springing into existence each minute.* "The story of the brain's structure begins at the start of life itself. Three weeks after conception, a single sheet of cells—no bigger than the tip of a paper match head—appears on the upper back of the human embryo. From this neural plate of a hundred thousand cells, the human brain folds itself into being. The plate curves into a groove, then closes into a tube. Furiously it grows, bulging here, elongating there, sprouting everywhere, at an average rate of 250,000 cells a minute." Jack Fincher, *The Brain: Mystery of Matter and Mind* (Washington, DC: U.S. News Books, 1981), 40.

26. *Roger Sperry's research.* Steven Rose, *The Conscious Brain* (New York: Vintage Books, 1976), 205–8.
27. *Helen's experience with her doll.* Helen Keller, *The Story of My Life* (New York: Doubleday, Page & Company, 1904), 24.
28. *How using particular brain cells forms and fashions the brain.* Judith Hooper and Dick Teresi, *Three-Pound Universe* (New York: Macmillan Publishing Company, 1986), 63–66. See also M. Hofer and Y. Barde, "Brain-derived neurotrophic factor prevents neuronal death *in vivo*," *Nature* 331 (January 21, 1988): 261–62.
29. *Joseph Campbell's description of the mythological journey.* Joseph Campbell, *The Hero with a Thousand Faces* (Princeton, NJ: Princeton Univ. Press,1968).
30. *"The godly powers sought . . ."* Ibid., 39, italics added.
31. *"We differ, blind and seeing . . ."* Keller, *The World I Live in,* 84, 86 (ellipses omitted).
32. *Origin of the word* wisdom. Eric Partridge, *Origins: A Short Etymological Dictionary of Modern English,* 4th ed. (New York: Macmillan Publishing Company, 1966), 778–79.
33. *Verse in Proverbs.* Proverbs 3:15 (King James translation).
34. *On using Viktor Frankl while he's still living.* I first wrote the story assuming Viktor Frankl had passed away. When my ever-alert editor, Lyle Fletcher, caught my error, I was oddly dismayed: while I was pleased to discover Viktor Frankl was living, I couldn't imagine the story without his thoughts. No matter. I simply rewrote the Frankl

section with Ben *quoting* Viktor's words. But it now had all the excitement of a three-day-old helium birthday balloon, baggy and puckered, hanging about a foot off the floor, sinking slowly, about to die. I needed to feel the spirit of Viktor *himself* saying the words. But did I dare put words into the mouth of a *living* person, particularly in a book that expresses so personal a philosophy?

I decided, obviously, that I did. I hope that Viktor Frankl, should he read what I have written about him, will be pleased. I intend only to honor him. He was, in fact, a source of my inspiration for the philosophy the story portrays. His words in the story either paraphrase or quote directly words from his book, and in his book those words support themes similar to mine. Frankl wrote, for example, "I think the meaning of our existence is not invented by ourselves, but rather detected. . . . A man's concern, even his despair, over the worthwhileness of life is a *spiritual distress*. . . . Each situation in life represents a challenge to man and presents a problem for him to solve. . . . The majority [of people] consider themselves accountable before God; they . . . do not interpret their own lives merely in terms of a task assigned to them but also in terms of the taskmaster who has assigned it to them." Viktor E. Frankl, *Man's Search for Meaning: An Introduction to Logotherapy* (New York: Pocket Books, 1963), 157, 163, 172, 174.

Despite these parallels, I am obviously responsible for the way I have used Viktor

Frankl's words and ideas, and I do not intend to suggest that he would necessarily agree with all aspects of the philosophy that I present.

35. *Viktor Frankl's imaginary lecture.* Ibid., 116–17.

36. *"Most men in a concentration camp . . ."* Ibid., 115.

37. *Origin of the word* dominion. Partridge, 162–63.

38. *"We who lived in concentration camps . . ."* Frankl, 104.

39. "We must picture Hell as a state where everyone is perpetually concerned about his own dignity and advancement, where everyone has a grievance, and where everyone lives the deadly serious passions of envy, self-importance, and resentment." C. S. Lewis, *The Screwtape Letters* (New York: Macmillan Publishing, 1961), ix.

40. *"Life ultimately means . . ."* Frankl, 122.

41. *On the idea that government has no personal answers.* "The legitimate object of government is 'to do for the people what needs to be done, but which they can not, by individual effort, do at all, or do so well, for themselves.' There are many such things—some of them exist independently of the injustice in the world. Making and maintaining roads, bridges, and the like; providing for the helpless young and afflicted; common schools; and disposing of deceased men's property, are instances. But a far larger class of objects springs from the injustice of men. If one people will make war upon another, it is a necessity . . . to unite and cooperate for defense. Hence the military department. If some men will kill, or beat, or constrain others, or despoil them of

property, by force, fraud, or noncomplicance with contracts, it is a common object with peaceful and just men to prevent it. Hence the criminal and civil departments." Lincoln, 2:221–22.

42. *"This most beautiful system of the sun . . . "* Isaac Newton, "Mathematical Principles of Natural Philosophy," in vol. 34 of *The Great Books* (Chicago: Encyclopedia Britannica, 1988), 369–70 (ellipses omitted).

43. *"MAN, fearfully and wonderfully made . . ."* Chisholm v. Georgia, 2 U.S. 419, 455 (1793).

44. *"those principles of abstract justice . . ."* Johnson and Graham's Lessee v. William M'Intosh, 21 U.S. 543, 572 (1823).

45. *"the source of eternal justice . . ."* Rhode Island v. Massachusetts, 39 U.S. 210, 225 (1840).

46. *"Out of the domain of the exact sciences . . ."* Hopt v. Utah, 120 U.S. 430, 439 (1887).

47. *On the assumptions underlying the Constitution being changed without due process.* My insights on this point come mainly from many personal conversations with Matthew M. F. Hilton, J.D, Ph.D., and from his dissertation, "A Preliminary Examination of the Contextual Framework of Opinions of the United States Supreme Court (1790–1987) and Its Relevance in the Evaluation of the Constitutionality of State Required Moral Education" (Ph.D. diss, Brigham Young University, 1989). Hilton refers to the four cases cited above in appendix 4 of his dissertation.

In the story, Isaac Newton describes a more abrupt change in assumptions than actually occurred. Hilton's dissertation carefully traces the history of the changes, pointing out, for example, that in 1892, five years after the 1887 decision cited science as the only source of certain truth, the Court nevertheless affirmed in another decision that "this is a religious nation." <u>Holy Trinity Church v. United States</u>, 143 U.S. 457, 470, 471 (1892). Nevertheless, the change was well underway, culminating roughly in the 1940s, though it continues even today to become more firmly entrenched. Under the original assumption, the people submitted to the will of God and the government submitted to the will of the people. Under the new assumption, God vanishes, leaving the people and the government to work out who will guide and who will submit. This is the context in which science, almost by default, has become the only source of absolute truth. If science is the only source of truth and government preempts science (or *vice versa*), by what principle will ordinary people prevail?

48. *"I was able to calculate in two hours . . ."* "Kepler's empirical formulation of the laws of planetary motion represents some sixty man-years of research (thirty years of Tycho Brahe's observations and thirty years of Kepler's arithmetic analysis), whereas Newton's derivation took only an hour or two. Moreover, this derivation from the law of gravity shows that Kepler's version of the third law is slightly incorrect and replaces Kepler's approximate statement of the third law by its correct statement." Lloyd Motz, "Introduction," in Jefferson Hane Weaver, ed., *The World of Physics: A Small Library of the*

*Literature of Physics from Antiquity to the
Present*, 3 vols. (New York: Simon and Schuster,
1987), 1:19.
49. *Alexander Pope's epitaph for Newton.* Cited in
Ilya Prigogine and Isabelle Stengers, *Order out of
Chaos: Man's New Dialogue with Nature* (New
York: Bantam Books, 1984), 27. Prigogine won
the Nobel Prize for chemistry in 1977.
50. *Poem about Newton by Ampere's son.* Ibid., 67.
51. *On the principle illustrated by ice turning into
water.* The change from ice to water illustrates a
"phase transition." All systems, including living
bodies and human societies, undergo predictable
phase transitions as they move varying distances
from equilibrium. Distance from equilibrium is
altered by adjusting "external control para-
meters," or factors that govern the energy flow.
    "When an external parameter is changed . . .
the system can pass through a variety of patterns."
Stig Lundqvist et al., eds., *Order and Chaos in
Nonlinear Physical Systems* (New York: Plenum
Press, 1988), 16.
    "The feature common to these phenomena is
that, as some external parameter . . . is varied, the
behavior of the system changes from simple to
erratic." M. J. Feigenbaum, "Universal behavior in
nonlinear systems," in D. Campbell and H. Rose,
eds., *Order in Chaos* (Amsterdam: North-Holland
Publishing, 1983), 17.
    "The aim of the theory is not to predict the
changes in the system in terms of the interactions
among particles; it aims instead to predict how
the system will react to modifications we may

impose on it from the outside." Prigogine and Stengers, 106.

52. *On the idea that far-from-equilibrium systems can't be predicted in the usual sense and on the general failure of deterministic "laws" of science.* "So the 'inexorable laws of physics' on which—for instance—Marx tried to model his laws of history, were never really there." Tim Poston and Ian Stewart cited in Ian Stewart, *Does God Play Dice?: The Mathematics of Chaos* (Oxford, England: Basil Blackwell, 1989), 40.

"The deterministic laws of physics, which were at one point the only acceptable laws, today seem like gross simplifications, nearly a caricature of evaluation." Ilya Prigogine, *From Being to Becoming: Time and Complexity in the Physical Sciences* (San Francisco: W. H. Freeman, 1980), xvii.

"The deterministic view of chemistry fails when far-from-equilibrium processes are involved. . . . The Golden Age of Classical Science is gone, and with it also the conviction that Newtonian rationality, even with its various conflicting interpretations, forms a suitable basis for our dialogue with nature." Prigogine and Stengers, 177, 29.

53. *On the idea that the idealized experiments don't actually describe real systems.* "The physicist has to limit himself very severely: he must content himself with describing the most simple events which can be brought within the domain of our experience; all events of a more complex order are beyond the power of the human intellect to

reconstruct with the subtle accuracy and logical perfection which the theoretical physicist demands. Supreme purity, clarity, and certainty at the cost of completeness. But what can be the attraction of getting to know such a tiny section of nature thoroughly, while one leaves everything subtler and more complex shyly and timidly alone?" Quote from Albert Einstein, cited in Prigogine and Stengers, 52.

"The classical emphasis on explicit solutions leads us to study systems that are not truly representative." Stewart, 253.

"Mathematicians . . . have increasing chosen to flee from nature by devising theories unrelated to anything we can see or feel." Benoit V. Mandelbrot, *The Fractal Geometry of Nature* (San Francisco: W. H. Freeman, 1982), 1.

54. *On the idea that things considered proved by double-blind research often turn out later to be disproved by experience.* "More than half the prescription drugs approved by the Food and Drug Administration (FDA) between 1976 and 1985 caused serious side effects that later caused the drugs to be either relabeled or removed from the market, according to a General Accounting Office (GAO) study released yesterday.

"The side effects included reactions that could cause hospitalization, disability and even death. . . .

"The GAO report found that these side effects were common—from a wide range of drugs for treating almost everything from infertility to heart disease—and fairly serious. They resulted in hospitalization, permanent disability, and even death.

"The report also found that . . . drugs approved for children were twice as likely to have serious post-approval risks than other medications." M. Gladwell, "Serious side effects linked to many approved drugs," *Washington Post,* May 28, 1990.

55. *"On freedom being denied on "scientific" grounds.* I have in mind experiences like the following. I phoned the director of the government division that licenses health practitioners in our state and told him about research published in the journal *Cancer.* The research was done at the University of Texas, and it showed Chinese herbs restoring natural immunity in cancer patients. Y. Sun et al., "Immune restoration and/or augmentation of local graft versus host reaction by traditional Chinese medicinal herbs," *Cancer* 52 (July 1, 1983), 70–73.

I asked the director something like this: One of the researchers on that project was an herb expert from China. Now, suppose one of my children got cancer. Could I invite that Chinese herb expert into my home to treat my child with his herbs?

The director's answer, in essence, was this: If the Chinese herb expert tried to treat my child with herbs, even at my request and in my own home, he would be guilty of a felony crime.

I asked him under what circumstance the Chinese herb expert could legally treat my child.

The director told me this: If I could find a licensed physician interested in using the herbs, that physician could file a plan with the hospital where he worked, and ask the institutional review board to review it. Only if the board approved the plan, and only if the physician filed all the proper informed-consent forms, could he proceed. The physician, not the Chinese herb expert, would have to do the treating, and he would have to prove that he was operating within the standards and ethics of medical science. Otherwise he risked losing his medical license. Few physicians would try it, the director said, because "I think they're afraid."

Next I looked up the state code covering child neglect. Section 17 of *Utah Code Annotated* 78-3A-2 says, " 'Neglected child' includes: . . . (c) A child whose parent, guardian, or custodian fails or refuses to provide proper or necessary . . . medical care . . . or any other care necessary for his health . . ." Then I called the juvenile court and asked the clerk: If I wanted to treat my sick child with herbs instead of drugs, could the state force me to submit to the medical authorities. She said that it happens all the time. If parents refuse to submit in such cases, the state has authority to deny them custody of their child.

The difference in such cases is that medicine fits the orthodox scientific model; herbs don't.

56. *On the idea that the orthodox methods of deterministic science don't work for far-from-equilibrium systems like bodies and societies.* "The scientist does not do as he pleases, and he cannot force nature to say only what he wants to hear. He cannot, at least in the long run, project upon it his most cherished desires and expectations. He

actually runs a greater risk and plays a more dangerous game the better his tactics succeed in encircling nature, in setting it more squarely with its back to the wall." Prigogine and Stengers, 43.

"I doubt if there has ever been a period in history when a greater proportion of people have found themselves frankly puzzled by the way the world reacts to their best efforts to change it, if possible for the better. . . . Recently [things] seem to have been going wrong so often and in so many different contexts, that many people are beginning to feel that they must be thinking in some wrong way about how the world works. I believe that this suspicion is probably correct. The ways of looking at things that we have in the past accepted as common sense . . . do not match the type of processes which are going on in the world at large." Conrad H. Waddington, *Tools for Thought* (New York: Basic Books, 1977), xi; see also 64–65.

57. *On the idea that the linking of science and government flows naturally from the classical deterministic model*. "The man of science . . . now becomes a kind of magician, a man apart, the potential holder of a universal key to all physical phenomena, thus endowed with a potentially omnipotent knowledge." Prigogine and Stengers, 21.

"As the nineteenth century closed, belief in reductionism and mechanism prevailed, but the price paid for this was high. Humankind now saw itself as the product of an improbable collision of particles following indifferent universal laws. Dethroned as offspring of the gods, humans reenthroned themselves as the possessors of knowledge about those laws. By knowing the laws, it was thought, we would learn with increasing deftness to predict and control the entropy [i.e., the tendency toward disorder] that afflicted complicated systems." John Briggs and F. David Peat, *Turbulent Mirror: An Illustrated Guide to Chaos Theory and the Science of Wholeness* (New York: Harper & Row, 1989), 23.

"Since the Second World War, science—or more exactly scientific research—has become a political factor to which all countries pay the greatest attention. . . . The organization of research tends increasingly to be centralized, and to come entirely under the control, direct or indirect, of the state." Jean Ladriere, *The Challenge Presented to Cultures by Science and Technology* (Paris: UNESCO, 1977), 19.

58. *UNESCO document.* Cited in Prigogine and Stengers, 30.
59. *Chaos theory references.* See, for example, James Gleick, *Chaos: Making a New Science* (New York: Viking Penguin, 1987); and Briggs and Peat.
60. *On the idea that self-regulation emerges in systems that exist far from equilibrium.* "Nonlinear interactions at critical values [i.e., distances from equilibrium] don't produce chaos, they produce spontaneous self-organizing forms." Briggs and Peat, 120.

"We know today that both the biosphere as a whole as well as its components, living or dead, exist in far-from-equilibrium conditions. In this context life, far from being outside the natural order, appears as the supreme expression of the self-organizing processes that occur." Prigogine and Stengers, 175.

61. *On the idea that the principles described apply throughout all aspects of nature.* "One of the exciting aspects of the new mathematical models in nonlinear dynamics is the wide applicability of these paradigms to many fields of science. Thus, it is no surprise that dynamic phenomena in biological systems that have exhibited chaotic motions, have been explained by some of the same equations used in electrical and mechanical science." Francis C. Moon, *Chaotic Vibrations: An Introduction for Applied Scientists and Engineers* (New York: John Wiley & Sons, 1987), 118.

"Most measurable properties of *any* such system . . . can be determined, in a way that essentially bypasses the details of the equations governing each specific system because the theory of this behavior is universal over such details." Feigenbaum, 17.

"A certain notion of the nonlinear dynamics of various processes, irrespective of the domain of physics to which they belong, is now being formed. Some common physical concepts have appeared, independent of the specific domain of application." R. Z. Sagdeev et al., *Nonlinear Physics: From the Pendulum to Turbulence and Chaos* (New York: Harwood Academic Publishlers, 1988), xx.

62. *On the idea that the writers of the Constitution saw themselves delegating rights of government*

based on a more fundamental power that resided with the people. Under James Madison's direction, the Constitutional convention began with the idea that governments are constructed on "social contracts." According to this idea, power belonged by natural right to the people, who would then establish a contract with their rulers that would specify which powers were delegated to those rulers and which were not. However:

> As the debate progressed, a new concept of government began more and more to be tossed around. It abandoned the whole idea of the contract between rulers and the ruled as the philosophic basis for government. It said instead that as power resided solely in the people, they could delegate as much as they wanted to, and withdraw it as they saw fit. All members of the government, not just legislators, would represent the people. The Constitution, thus, was not a bargain between the people and whoever ran the new government, but a delegation of certain powers to the new government, which the people could revise whenever they wanted. . . . Under the new idea, the governors are not partners, but the servants of the governed. The people could alter the arrangement; the government could not. Christopher Collier and James Lincoln Collier, *Decision in Philadelphia: The Constitutional Convention of 1787* (New York: Ballantine Books, 1987), 285–86.

About the Author

Dean Black received a Ph.D. degree from Pennsylvania State University and is listed in *American Men and Women of Science*. He has taught at the University of Southern California and Brigham Young University and currently writes and lectures on topics related to natural health and philosophies of living.

For information about additional Tapestry Press products by Dean Black, call toll-free, 1-800-333-4290.